P9-DEB-740

SCHOLASTIC
ART & WRITING AWARDS
PRESENTS

# THE
# BEST
# TEEN
# WRITING
# OF
# 2018

*Edited by*
**Romaissaa Benzizoune**
2016 American Voices Nominee
and Gold Medal Recipient

**Scholastic
Art & Writing
Awards**

For information or permission, contact:
Alliance for Young Artists & Writers
557 Broadway
New York, NY 10012
**artandwriting.org**

No part of this publication may be reproduced in whole or
in part, or stored in a retrieval system, or transmitted in
any form or by any means, including electronic, mechanical,
photocopying, microfilming, recording, or otherwise, without
written permission from the publisher.

Editor: Romaissaa Benzizoune
Managing Editor: Hannah Jones
Director, Programs: Debra Samdperil
Design Director: Meg Callery
Production Manager and Proofreader: Jean-Paul Bass
Copy Editor: Ingrid Accardi
Production Assistant: Helen Canales

Front and back cover: *Baboon in a Sunny Room*, Painting by
Bailey Bunick, Grade 12, Age 17, Lake Oswego High School,
Lake Oswego, OR

© 2018 Alliance for Young Artists & Writers
All rights reserved. Printed in the United States of America
Anthology printing, August 2018
ISBN13: 978-1-338-35802-5

## DEDICATION

*The Best Teen Writing of 2018* is dedicated to Mark O'Grady, esteemed professor at Pratt Institute and Alumnus of the Scholastic Art & Writing Awards. His dedication to the creative voice of young people has brought to light the brilliance of tens of thousands of young artists and writers over the past decade.

Mark's commitment to the Alliance for Young Artists & Writers is all-encompassing, and he holds a special place in its history. He has served as a Regional and National Art Juror, and he's hosted adjudication sessions, workshops, and panel discussions. Most importantly, Mark has built a welcoming space for Scholastic Awards students and educators at Pratt Institute.

After receiving his Scholastic Award, Mark graduated with honors from the Cooper Union School of Art and then received an MFA degree from Louisiana Tech University. He is an internationally exhibiting artist and is currently a full-time professor at Pratt Institute.

## TABLE OF CONTENTS

III   Dedication

IX   About *The Best Teen Writing of 2018*

X   About the Scholastic Art & Writing Awards

XII   National Writing Jurors

XVI   Editor's Introduction

### Gold Medal Portfolio Awards

2   *For the Love of God,* Kush Dhungana

6   *Weekends on the Moon,* Alexandra Swerdloff

8   *Smudge,* Malachi Jones

10   *The Couch,* Osarugue Otebele

13   *The Sketchbook,* Sam Wachman

18   *Millennial Love,* Sarena Kuhn

21   *Token,* Triniti Wade

26   *Evolution,* Vicky Brown

27   *Ocean Tables,* Osarugue Otebele

### Special Achievement and American Voices Awards

30   *Origin Story,* Sophie Paquette

33   *Shaving Cream,* Victoria Gong

35   *Three Shots Through the Window of a Synagogue in Indiana,* Daniel Blokh

36   *Six Definitions for American,* Eileen Huang

39   *The Lunatic (A Pantoum),* Noah Trevino

40   *Terrorist,* Neelam Bohra

43   *The Hope for the Best,* Eliseo Corona

49   *Defrauding or Discriminating: The Constitutionality of Voter Identification Laws in the 21st Century,* Nathan Zhao

59   *The Mourning Of,* Kendall Vorhis

**Science Fiction & Fantasy**

62  *Ten*, Catarina Chung

67  *Leaving Silence*, Devony Hof

**Critical Essay**

74  *The Permanence of Plastic*, Meghna Pamula

79  *What "Finsta" Culture Says About Modern Teenagers*, Julia Spande

83  *Lannister Policies in Counterinsurgency*, Jackson Ehrenworth

92  *This Is Us, It Always Has Been*, Ryan Kim

**Dramatic Script**

95  *The Worst Kind of Goodbye*, Maya Robles

98  *Kings of Men*, Mollie Pate

**Flash Fiction**

105  *Coffee*, Eunice Choi

108  *Talk*, Georgia Flanders

111  *Stovetop Glow*, Megan Lunny

114  *Gwen*, Amrita Vetticaden

117  *Sarcophagus*, Annika Clark

119  *Ocean Eyes*, Jessica Liu

123  *Transmissions from the Satellite Heart*, Leyla Ebrahimi

**Journalism**

126  *"Just Another Day in Hurricane City": Surviving Hurricane Irma*, Alexandra Byrne

132  *The Coder's Code*, Geoffrey Brann

135  *Through Grace's Eyes*, Georgia Greenblum

142  *Paola Gonzalez: A Dreamer in the Land of the Free*, Sheharbano Jafry

**Novel Writing**

150  *Fishbowl*, Luke Herzog

**Personal Essay & Memoir**

154  *The Mexican-American Dictionary of Familial Communication*, Isabel Estrada

158  *Jones Beach*, Kalley Huang

161  *Last Words*, Laila Shadid

166  *My Grandmother's Bones*, Ananya Ganesh

173  *Truths I'm Trying to Ignore*, Sophya Giudici-Juarez

176  *Embracing Frankenstein*, Nick Johnson

179  *Under the Shade of the Apple Tree*, Myra Kamal

183  *My Cousin Ethan*, Maxwell Surprenant

**Poetry**

186  *Citric*, Alexis DePinho

187  *Instructions for Building a Nation*, Amma Otchere

190  *Nothing but the Truth*, Charlie Hastings

193  *Fur Trading*, Christopher Barlow

196  *Where I'm From*, Crystal Centeno-Padilla

198  *My Mother's Favorite Drugstore Wine*, Kate Grayson

199  *My Voice, a Burden to You*, Maddy Barker

200  *Blk Girl Depression*, Nahisha Jackson

203  *After Harvey*, Rukmini Kalamangalam

204  *Untitled*, Akilah Toney

205  *Sky People*, Salihah Aakil

206  *Body Writings*, William Lohier

208  *When Black Kids Time Travel, They Don't—*, Zain-Minkah Murdock

211  *Bulletproof Scarf*, Akhiyar Abdi

213  *Deconstruction*, Danelle Antelo

**Short Story**

214 *Labor of Love*, Brinda Rao

220 *At the Tone*, Isabella Eraula

225 *Fixing a Whole*, Daniela Ceja

229 *The Waves*, Simone Gulliver

235 *Breaking and Entering*, Jeehwan Kim

239 *Burial*, Ty Kiatathikom

**Humor**

243 *A Satire on Suburbia*, Ani Freedman

246 *How to Look More Asian: A Guide to Becoming an Exotic Geisha or Your Favorite K-pop Star*, Emily Jiang

252 *Unqualified: A Women's Glossary*, Shaun-Marley Duncan

255 *Update to Community Regarding Rich White Liberal Suburban School District's Sky-High Test Scores*, Michael Cheng

261 *Do Not Compare Me to a Summer's Day*, Gabriel Sánchez Ainsa

266 *Letter to My Substitute*, Trevor Zavac

271 About the Authors

281 Educators List

287 Educator's Guide

291 Regional Affiliates

301 Acknowledgements

302 Thank You

**CLARA KROHN**, *Sun and Moon*, Painting. Grade 9, Age 15, Archbishop Hoban High School, Akron, OH. Jill Fortman, *Educator*

## ABOUT THE BEST TEEN WRITING OF 2018

The pieces featured in *The Best Teen Writing of 2018* were selected from works that earned National Medals in the 2018 Scholastic Art & Writing Awards. The Scholastic Awards, a national program presented by the Alliance for Young Artists & Writers, identifies and showcases teenagers with exceptional artistic and literary talent. Founded in 1923, the program celebrates the accomplishments of creative students and extends opportunities for recognition, exhibition, publication, and scholarships.

This year, nearly 1,050 students earned National Medals in writing categories. The works selected for this publication represent the diversity of the National Medalists, including age and grade, gender, genre, geography, and subject matter. They also present a spectrum of the insight and creative intellect that inform many of the pieces.

A complete listing of National Medalists and online galleries of awarded works of art and writing can be found on our website, **artandwriting.org**. Visit our site to see how to enter the 2019 Scholastic Art & Writing Awards, as well as a list of our scholarship partners and ways you can partner with the Alliance to support young artists and writers in your community.

Some of the writing selections have been excerpted. Go to **artandwriting.org/galleries** to read all of the work as it was submitted.

## ABOUT THE SCHOLASTIC ART & WRITING AWARDS

Since 1923, the Scholastic Art & Writing Awards have recognized the vision, ingenuity, and talent of our nation's youth, and provided opportunities for creative teens to be celebrated. Each year, increasing numbers of teens participate in the program and become a part of our community—young artists and writers, filmmakers and photographers, poets and sculptors, video game artists and science fiction writers—along with countless educators who support and encourage the creative process. Notable Scholastic Awards alumni include Andy Warhol, Sylvia Plath, Cy Twombly, John Baldessari, Ken Burns, Kay WalkingStick, Richard Avedon, Stephen King, Luis Jiménez, Paul Chan, Marc Brown, Truman Capote, and Joyce Carol Oates—to name just a few.

### Our Mission

The Scholastic Art & Writing Awards are presented by the Alliance for Young Artists & Writers. The Alliance is a 501(c)(3) nonprofit organization whose mission is to identify students with exceptional artistic and literary talent and present their remarkable work to the world through the Scholastic Art & Writing Awards. Through the Awards, students receive opportunities for recognition, exhibition, publication, and scholarships. Students across America submitted nearly 350,000 original works during our 2018 program year across 29 different categories of art and writing.

### Our Programs

Through the Scholastic Awards, teens in grades 7–12 from public, private, or home schools can apply in 29 categories of art and writing for a chance to earn scholarships and have their works exhibited and published. Beyond the Awards, the Alliance for Young Artists & Writers produces a number of programs to support creative students and their educators, including the Art.Write.Now.Tour, the National Student Poets Program, the Scholastic Awards Summer Workshops and Scholastic Awards Summer Scholarships programs, the Golden Educators Residency, and many more. The Alliance features works by National Medalists of both art and writing in our annual National Catalog. Additionally, we publish a collection of exemplary written works in this anthology, *The Best Teen Writing*, and a chapbook that features works from the National Student Poets. These publications are distributed free of charge to schools, students, educators, museums, libraries, and arts organizations across the country.

## 2018 SCHOLASTIC ART & WRITING AWARDS
## NATIONAL WRITING JURORS

### American Voices
Hasan Altaf
H.G. Carrillo
Wo M. Chan
Josh Dale
Cristina Garcia
Tyehimba Jess
Alvina Ling
Aimee C. Nezhukumatathil
Erlina D. Ortiz
Kamran Pasha
Davy Rothbart
Kate Rushin
Rene Saldana
Duncan Tonatiuh
Yolanda Wisher

### Best-in-Grade
Opal Palmer Adisa
Paige Britt
Maggie Brown
Ann E. Burg
Marisa Ann Conner
Ron Currie
Thomas Sayers Ellis
Joshua Furst
Darlene White Harris
Dave Housley
Joseph O. Legaspi

Matthew Limpede
Carson Moss
Alix Ohlin
Tommy Pico
Vijay Seshadri
David van Belle
Richard Van Camp

### Civic Expression Award
Emma Adelman
Ami Aronson
Cristina Domenech
Louise Dube
Alexis Fajardo
Allison Granucci
King Grossman
David Hassler
Cole Lavalais
John Oakes
Jeffrey Shotts
Connor White

### Critical Essay
Emelie Lucille Elizabeth
   Chhangur
Janet Konstant
Brett Fletcher Lauer
Eesha Pandit
Lauren Redniss

Elizabeth D. Samet
Mara Shalloup
Russell Shorto
Marisa Siegel

**Dramatic Script**
Jennifer Hamburg
Tina Mabry
Dante Russo

**Flash Fiction**
Jeffery Renard Allen
Danielle Bennett
John Bloomberg-Rissman
Carmen Agra Deedy
Aimee Friedman
Myla Goldberg
Barbara Kerley
J. Robert Lennon
Brenda Maier
John Schreiber
Salvatore Scibona

**Humor**
Moira Bailey
William Evans
Negin Farsad
Dionna Griffin-Irons
Omar Holmon
Mark Pett

Baratunde Thurston
Sheng Wang

**Journalism**
Rosella Fabbri
John Leland
Rossella May-Hartwell

**New York Life Award**
Julie Berry
Cathy Linh Che
Amy S. Choi
Laurel F. Crosby
Josh Funk
Ravi Howard
Amorak Huey
Paul Lisicky
Richard L. Lopez
Allison Moore
Matt Morton
Mi'Jan Celie Tho-Biaz

**Novel Writing**
Matthew J. Kirby
Rodman Philbrick
Olugbemisola
    Rhuday-Perkovich

**Personal Essay & Memoir**
Harlyn G. Aizley
Daniel P. Ehrenhaft
James Walter Doyle

Sade Falebita
Manuel Gonzalez
Timothy Liu
Dania Martinez
Andrew McCarthy
Okey A. Ndibe
Jennifer A. Nielson
Kode Jamil Ransom
Eliot John Schrefer
Gary Soto
Sergio Troncoso
OJ Williams
Kyndal Nichelle Wilson

### Poetry

Li Yun Alvarado
Oliver Baez Bendorf
Mahogany L. Browne
Christopher Richard Carmona
Ama Codjoe
Henri Cole
Marlene E. Graham
Myrlin Hepworth
Patricia Kennedy
Lo Kwa Mei-en
Leonardo Nin
Brian A. Sonia-Wallace
Alok Vaid-Menon
Hubert Vigilla
Ocean Vuong
Hanif Willis-Abdurraqib
Jose Javier Zamora

### Science Fiction & Fantasy

Rion Amilcar Scott
Ann VanderMeer
Jeff VanderMeer

### Short Story

Brianna Albers
Annabeth Bondor-Stone
Kheryn Callender
Sarwat Chadda
Max Gladstone
Estella Gonzalez
Shannon Hitchcok
Cihan Kaan
Greg Kishbaugh
Bill Konigsberg
Sara B. Larson
Chigozie Obioma
Princess Perry
Augusta R. Scattergood
Patricia Smith
Sunil Yapa

### Writing Portfolio

David Andersson
Rebecca Bondor
Randy Brown
Kayombo Chingonyi
Anthony Michael D'Aries
Betty Harris
Lynn Harris
David A. Hernandez

Angel Kimble
Lisa Lucas
Sarah Manguso
Kenn Nesbitt
Gerald A. Padilla
Laura Pegram
Cameron Pierce
Alice Quinn
Trent Reedy
L.B. Schulman
Laura Tisdel
Linda Vasu

**Romaissaa Benzizoune**
*2016 American Voices Nominee*
*and Gold Medal Recipient*

For many of us Americans, 2018 has been exhausting. We have been exhausted by the world and its antics; by men with political power and by men without; by the very act of witnessing. We have been exhausted by the way some of our identities remain erased in this country, while others rear their dark heads at critical moments to exemplify our silence and complicity.

The work you are holding is perhaps a more honorable reaction to 2018.

The spirit of this collection is fiery, extraordinarily brave, and (above all) ready. Ready for something better; ready to make it so. A young journalist rivals the work of professionals when she tackles the story of a dreamer who loves to run. A young writer fights generations of Orientalism with a hilarious guide on "how to look more Asian" (in which Scarlett Johansson, Emma Stone, and Tilda Swinton are directed to skip all instruction and collect their movie roles anyway). Another young writer candidly assesses the process of building and maintaining this great nation: "Talk about this history in words that criss-cross like mismatched whip marks on a smooth expanse of skin . . . Call it rewritten."

You will soon realize that "teen" in *The Best Teen Writing of 2018* is not a qualifier but a challenge. (What are the rest of us doing?) You will be challenged to learn about the ethics of professional coding, about the effects of isolating children with disabilities from their peers in school, about why teen-agers increasingly choose finsta when they want to be real with you. You will be challenged to grapple with the intersec-tion of blackness, femininity, and depression (depression has reserved a parking spot marked/for spoiled white girls/dying for pity is their hobby). You will be challenged to imagine: a boy who speaks in Shakespeare; an asylum for the "wrongly afraid"; a group of astronauts who have just witnessed the implosion of their world from above.

This collection leaves me with no doubt: This is the genera-tion of BLM leaders and gun control advocates. This is the generation of those who champion the rights of the still oc-cupied, still colonized, and still oppressed everywhere. This is the generation that gives new meaning to the statement—tossed around like recycling and repeated into oblivion—that the future is in our youth.

Of course, to strip this collection down to the political would be to discredit the human emotions that transcend this year, this administration, this country, and all systems of power everywhere. The way that love in all its forms is captured and savored. A mother who just came home from work, her legs crossed on the back porch. A girl who loves a girl who adamantly doesn't love girls anymore. The taste of a blood orange, unraveling the peel. A childhood home, framed Virgen de Guadalupe photos on the wall.

Prepare to be inspired.

THEN, IT DROPPED IT.

**JULIA TALBOT**, *Moon Kingdom*, Comic Art. Grade 12, Age 18, Medford High School, Medford, MA. Candace Van Aken, *Educator*

## GOLD MEDAL PORTFOLIO

Graduating high school seniors may submit a portfolio of eight works for review by authors, educators, and literary professionals.

The eight recipients of the Gold Medal Writing Portfolio each receive a $10,000 scholarship.

Some of the writing selections have been excerpted.
Visit **artandwriting.org/galleries** to read all of the work as it was submitted.

# For the Love of God

**KUSH DHUNGANA**, Grade 12, Age 17. Livingston High School, Livingston, NJ. Susan Rothbard, *Educator*

INT. BEDROOM—NIGHT—FLASHBACK
[God is lying in bed, on His phone. Katie climbs in.]

KATIE
Babe, my day was so crazy today.

GOD
Really?

[As Katie continues to talk, God's phone buzzes. God tries to slyly take a peek at it.]

ANGLE ON—PHONE SCREEN
[A text message appears under the name of "SATAN." It reads: Reminder tht u suuuckk]

GOD
(under his breath)
So annoying.

KATIE (O.S.)
Wow. You're not even listening.

[God immediately looks back at Katie.]

GOD
No, no. I'm listening.

[Katie then lies down with her back facing God. God knows
that He screwed up.]

GOD (CONT'D)
Let there be flowers.

[Flowers appear in God's hand.]

KATIE
That's not gonna work.

INT. RESTAURANT—FLASHBACK
[God and Katie sit at a table.]

KATIE
Hey, so I was reading your book.

GOD
Isn't it great?

KATIE
It was fine . . . What was that part about when they said that
you are love?

GOD
Well, I am love.

KATIE
So, like, you love everyone?

GOD
Mm-hmm.

KATIE
So . . .
(pointing to random guy)
. . . you love that guy?

GOD
Yup.

KATIE
What about . . .
(points to different guy)
 . . . that guy?

GOD
Sure.

KATIE
What about . . .
(points to girl)
 . . . that waitress over th—

GOD
Yes.

KATIE
(pissed)
Why did you answer so quickly for her?

GOD
What?

KATIE
Do you think she's hot or something?

GOD
No . . . I mean, she's just . . . I was just saying that I love her.

KATIE
What?

GOD
B-but not really. She's nothing compared to you, sweetheart.

[Katie stares down a nervous God.]

INT. CAR—DAY
[Katie drives the car while God rides shotgun.]

GOD
Hey, babe.
(points out the window)
You see those trees over there?

KATIE
Yeah.

GOD
I made them. All of them, babe. I made all those trees.

KATIE
Yeah, I get it.

GOD
I've made, like, every tree.

KATIE
Uh-huh.

GOD
Babe, you see those shrubs over there?

[Katie sighs.]
[CUT TO BLACK]

# Weekends on the Moon

**ALEXANDRA SWERDLOFF,** Grade 12, Age 17. Boise High School, Boise, ID. Jennifer McClain, *Educator*

I spent the summer after my parents split up with my mom in the suburbs. My dad was hired by NASA, I told my friends, and my mom didn't want a long-distance relationship split between San Francisco and the moon. Or he'd joined the CIA, was off doing recon in faraway places with names I couldn't pronounce, and it was all very secretive and I wasn't even supposed to be telling anyone. He'd been cast in the next Bond movie. Was exploring the bottom of the ocean.

On weekends, Mom drove me into the city. Dad and I went to the movies, out to eat; the waitress stared at the spots on his face.

My dad works in Paris now, I told my friends. He takes me to visit sometimes.

When he got too weak to walk, I pushed his wheelchair around the neighborhood; he liked the feel of the sun on his face. Learned my own kind of French: kaposi sarcoma, pneumocystis pneumonia, too late, terminal. Sat on the floor of the sterilized hub of his own personal spaceship at San Francisco General Hospital, watching the day turn to dusk and then night from the window while my father, the astronaut, took measured sips of oxygen from the tank at his bedside.

How was the moon? my friends asked. How was Paris?

Dad's breathing got shorter. The spots on his skin multiplied. A heart port appeared on his chest.

Paris was great, I said.

Depending on who you asked, I spent my weekends on Mars, at the Pentagon, on a submarine. Until, one day, the phone call came.

That weekend, I stayed home.

What happened to the moon? my friends asked. What happened to Paris?

At night I went out into the backyard and stared up at the sky—at its unnumbered stars, distant planets, orbiting satellites. Watched the tiny blinking space stations, full of other people's fathers, travel their predetermined paths.

I didn't want to go, I said.

The moon is overrated, anyways.

# Smudge

**MALACHI JONES**, Grade 12, Age 17. Charleston County School of the Arts, North Charleston, SC. Danielle DeTiberus, Francis Hammes, and Elizabeth Hart, *Educators*

For His stripes, I might have received double.
And He never saved me from my beating.
He didn't flinch from that cross,
from Papa's neck. As He wept. I wept,
my bare chest and stomach pressed against
Papa's knee. Papa kept the cotton picking
arch in my back. I used to wonder why
his hands were so worn but his most enduring
labor was to "wear me out."

His job to "teach me what the world can't." To whip
out the spirit of disobedience. Power
is the rack of waist belts, sting of a slipper,
choosing your own switch—
too small, sharper swipes; too big, bigger
bruises. Why did I always pick too small? I still
got the bruises—"tough love" and
grandfather's black hand hoisted
in the air. That's what I thought power is,
but what it looks like is white

skin they didn't have but feared.
Grandma held me by the wrist when I was young
so this white world wouldn't kill me in my youth.
A good one is better than a dead one.

A bruised one better than a bloody one.
Mommy stripped me to my socks
so they wouldn't have to in prison, she made
a mirror of our past. Stripped down
on an auction block to show how
well behaved we were. How we were good
enough to never have to whip. I never
deserved to be whupped.

My elders or my massa, I don't know
who's who, because they both want to price me
high to this white world. The mirror they hold
to my face frightens me. My eyes see,
past, present, and future—the same
image. A black mass against a bright canvas

# The Couch

**OSARUGUE OTEBELE**, Grade 12, Age 16. Hollis F. Price Middle College
High School, Memphis, TN. Chandra Boddie and Diana Gentry, *Educators*

When her daddy left he took the couch
Where mama lost her other earring
Where her sister lost 30 cents
Where her brother had his first kiss
Where grandma took her last breath
Where her uncle explored the layers of her skin
Where her aunt saw the flowers dying, but chose to see no
evil
Where no one asked so she didn't tell

Where her cousins argued about thick girls
Asked her if she ate soul food, because she wasn't shaped like
a black girl
Where they got drunk and didn't care, that the things her
mother gave her hadn't come in yet
Where her mother told her about little boys
And closing her legs
Where she sat around the little boys and closed her legs
Where they were pulled apart, where she screamed, where
she said no but they heard no evil
When her cousins left they cried because they missed the
couch
Where they felt like men
Where they explored the deepest waters
Where they felt the rush to clean up their mess
Where they told her "hush it'll never happen again"

Where they told her "we're sorry it happened again"
Where they called her dumb for believing them again
Where they lost the TV remote digging into her skin
Changing channels in her mind
Where they hope she wouldn't tell
When her uncle left he laughed because
It wasn't just the couch
It was playing house too close to home
Tiptoeing, deciding to sleep in
SLIP IN
Not recognizing whose air he was breathing
His hands dancing around her skin
Where she almost yelled
Where he covered her mouth
Hush "you ain't got to do nothing back"
You don't wanna make your uncle mad
Then I'll have to whoop ya
And I'll make sure it hurt more than this
When her daddy left he took the couch
Where her mama told her to stop dressing like a Thot
That she would attract unwanted attention
Where she asked her mama if that was what attracted her
uncle's and cousin's attention
Where her mama slapped her because they could do no evil
They could part no seas, but yet red is all she saw
When her daddy left she yelled. Mama
When you left, they would take me outside
Let me play
Bring me inside, and said they needed to play too
Mama they made my insides hurt and I saw something you
said I was only supposed to see when I got older
I didn't feel like a woman . . .

I felt so little, hot.
Uncle's sweat dripping on my skin
Kinda cooled me down.
Before you came, they cleaned up the mess
I wanted to tell, but you always said uncle was a god-fearing
man
And god-fearing men don't play ring around the rosy
And leave burning between your legs
They don't continue their last supper as you continue their
lord's prayers
Don't make you their mary, how do you explain this jesus to
your people
When her daddy left he took the couch where she became a
woman
Saw the blood soak into the couch
Ran to the bathroom
Saw it run down her legs.
Shuddered her shoulders
Didn't tell her mother. She knew how to be a woman
When her daddy left to burn the couch he took his bible
He wanted to wipe his hands clean of all sin

# The Sketchbook

**SAM WACHMAN**, Grade 12, Age 17. Cambridge Rindge & Latin High School, Cambridge, MA. Ariel Maloney, *Educator*

### 2012

"How big do you think the universe is?"

Out here, the sky is close. If I were a little taller, I think I could reach out and steal a constellation—just a small one. Maybe Delphinus or Sagitta—one nobody would notice was gone. Maybe I could take a pair of hedge clippers and prune the tail off Serpens Caput.

It's the first day of summer, and Teddy and I are lying in the grass of our valley, our secret place in the middle of the forest, looking at the stars.

"Really, really big," I answer. "Like, a million Americas. No, ten million. And my dad says it's always expanding."

"What's it expanding into?" he asks.

"Nothing."

"Like, empty space?"

"No, not even that. Nothing at all. Capital 'N' Nothing."

I can see him squinting in the flickering light of his lantern, trying his hardest to understand the entire universe all at once.

"I don't know what to picture when imagining capital 'N'

Nothing," he says. "I must be really stupid."

"I don't understand it either."

"Of course you do. You're Finn. You always understand everything."

I shake my head. "Not true."

He takes out his sketchbook and starts writing, or maybe drawing—I can never tell which. "What are you doing?"

"Nothing."

He redirects the lantern to shine on his sketchbook. The watery light grazes his back, mottled with welts and bruises.

"Where'd you get these?" I ask, poking at a particularly angry purple bruise. His whole body winces at my touch.

"You know that big pine tree over by the river?"

"Of course." It's one of the only trees around here we can climb—most of the trees in this forest have branches far too frail to support our weight.

"I fell out of it chasing away the pirates," he explains with his smile, sweet and mischievous all at once, the smile only he can ever pull off. "Don't worry. They'll be back for us to chase off together."

## 2014

"I don't know," Teddy says, clutching his sketchbook to his chest.

"Oh, come on," I beg. "You can't tell me you drew me and then not let me see it. Since when are you shy?"

"It's kind of my all-time favorite," he says. "And, at the same time, it feels kind of weird that I sketched it."

"You are kind of weird. Can I see it?"

I guess I understand how Teddy feels. Whenever people ask to see my writing, I feel like they're dissecting me, scrutinizing all of my internal organs.

But Teddy's always been different. I've never been afraid to let him dissect me. I've never been afraid to let him see everything hidden beneath my skin.

I wish he felt the same way about me.

"M-maybe someday," he stutters. "Want to go for a swim?"

When Teddy takes off his shirt at the edge of the lake, there's a bruise on his lower back.

"Fall out of a tree?"

"No," he says, and my heart sinks.

### 2016

"We knew it was coming," I say, just to fill the silence, even though I never really thought it would happen.

"Bullshit, Finn." Teddy rolls over in his sleeping bag. "They could have worked it out."

"Teddy."

"Without you, this place is nothing." He wipes his eyes. "Capital 'N' Nothing."

"Teddy, listen to me—"

"You're going to find someone else, someone better than me—"

I pull him closer, closer still, until my head is between his shoulder and his neck, where we fit together best, and we sit there for a moment, listening to the Earth turn. Just two boys at the end of the world.

"Did—" Teddy's voice breaks. He takes a deep breath, and starts again. "Did I ever tell you about that time we fought off those pirates?"

I laugh, lay back down and close my eyes.

"Tell me again," I whisper, my eyes burning with useless tears.

I wake up early the next morning into a story I have to end. I take one last look at him, still asleep in the sleeping bag printed with constellations I gave him for his fourteenth birthday—

his hair everywhere all at once, his side rising and falling with each deep breath, his hand still in mine from when we fell asleep together.

"I'm coming back for you," I whisper. I climb the hill out of our valley, out of our life together, and I say it again. I say it again when I get in Dad's truck, again when we cross the border into the next province, because there's always a chance that my words will blow through the air like dandelion seeds to wherever Teddy is right now—alone in our valley, on his bed wearing his paint-splattered hoodie, having adventures somewhere that never existed for anyone but us.

"I'm coming back for you." In the fading sunlight, I can just make out the blurred edge of the highway speeding by, and if I stare long enough, I can make myself forget whether it's me or the world moving.

The car hits a pothole and a familiar tattered book slides out of my bag. I open it to the inside cover.

Return to Teddy Cassidy, 7 East Farm Road.

The words "No peeking!" are scratched out and replaced by "Turn to page 72."

I flip through the book, my heartbeat speeding up with every increasing number scribbled in the corner of each page.

That Time Finn and I Fought Those Space Pirates

It's all here. Every last story, in words and sketches.

That Time Finn and I Met a Forest Spirit

Finally, I reach page 72, and my heart is down in my stomach, up in my throat, beating in my ears—everywhere but my chest.

There's the sketch he drew of me two years ago. It's better than perfect. He made my shaggy black hair a little less ugly, my always-dark eyes a little brighter.

He drew me like I was something beautiful.

Below the sketch, he wrote:

*Finn,*

*I know I tell a lot of stories. Some of them are true. Most of them aren't. To me, that never really mattered.*

*But there's one story that's better than the rest. Seriously, it makes the other ones look like knock-knock jokes. And, the best part is, it's true.*

*It's a long one, but it's a good one, so you'd better get started.*

*Presenting:*

*That Time I Fell in Love With the Boy With the Whole Universe in His Eyes*

I lay my head down on the car window, listening to the old complaints of the car's wheels bumping over the tattered asphalt of the road out of town, and I can't help but smile to myself as I let Teddy's stories fill me up once again.

# Millennial Love

**SARENA KUHN**, Grade 12, Age 17. Los Alamitos High School, Los Alamitos, CA. Karen Yoshihara-Ha, *Educator*

On occasion I will settle into bed on a Saturday night with a cup of tea, log in to my Netflix account, and find things not as I can last recall. Throughout the dealings of my day, a stranger has been lurking stealthily behind a screen—the evidence being left in my recently watched history. Some days I might discover that an entire movie marathon has taken place in my absence, or that my crucial pause in a thrilling series has been played and lost by a silent click. The antics of this parasite once irked me beyond measure, but I have since fallen into passive resignation.

Over the course of my life, I have shared my account password with a number of individuals. Ex-girlfriends, roommates, family members and the like have all benefited from my monthly payment of ten dollars, though I never complained. And most of these sojourners gradually left my account due to a loss of contact or necessity.

Still, one leech remains.

I don't think I would like to know who it is, for it would take away the amusement in my wondering. I like to think that she—a she because her identity can be anything I want so long as it's unknown—is a thrifty girl, perhaps an ex of my roommate or an acquaintance from dorm life. She lives alone in an apartment in the city—neither a high-end nor sketchy neighborhood. She works too hard for some start-up company, leaving her little time to develop a social life. I think she's frugal but successful. Although, she must not be successful enough to pay for her own Netflix account.

She's a fan of those artsy independent films. That's why I know it must be only one person: She's just too consistent in taste. But whenever I find myself trying to watch whatever obscure title she has left behind for me, I find an unsettling feeling just above my stomach. I cannot ever decide if the films are genius or contrived. Perhaps she feels the same.

If I'm in a particularly fanciful mood, I will craft elaborate narratives behind each of her selections. Just last week she booked a flight to Bali and was conducting research by watching documentaries about Indochina. I am also certain that for a month this year, she had been battling heartbreak—*The Vow*, *Sixteen Candles*, and *The Notebook* supporting this hypothesis. I knew she was over it when she returned to her quirky dramas and documentaries.

I'll say it again: I wouldn't want to meet her. Doing so might confirm my suspicion that the stranger really is a bum, or worse yet, someone whom I knew or know deeply. I feel as though I have been intruding upon her privacy for years by interpreting her tastes and considering recommendations never intended for me. It seems silly that I feel guilty toward the girl who stole my Netflix password. What if we met, and I discovered that she watched all these movies as meaningless white noise? That all of my inventions were false. And it would shatter a world—not necessarily an important one—if it turned out she was an old enemy or lover. If we were to meet, even if she turns out to be exactly the person I imagine, we would undoubtedly have to address that she has been benefiting from my monthly payments without consent. She would then probably discontinue her use (assuming she's a reasonable human being). But I'm not quite sure I want that.

Sometimes I find it unsettling when she pauses a film or episode at an unconventional time. Just the other day she stopped *Eternal Sunshine of the Spotless Mind* with 27 minutes and 3 seconds remaining. I'm then left to decide whether she found the movie too boring or a home intruder had shut the laptop with a gun against her neck at that very second. And so when she does this, I resume play and watch until the end, no matter what expository information is lost to me. Without words, I feel I've finished an important work for her, that we've shared an intimate conversation, that we've watched this movie together while upon a tired maroon loveseat with a bowl of buttered popcorn between us.

She probably thinks it's annoying.

# Token

**TRINITI WADE**, Grade 12, Age 17. School for Advanced Studies-North, Miami, FL. Frederick Green, *Educator*

Tasha Carter almost didn't mind being the only black girl in all of her classes, in all of her four years spent at Dalton Preparatory School. She almost didn't mind that, whenever her English class read their one mandatory novel in African-American literature each year, her teachers always called her out first, asking for her opinions on Toni Morrison's Pecola Breedlove or Zora Neale Hurston's Janie Crawford. She almost didn't mind when, during her junior year in AP United States History, her teacher wanted to know what she thought about the Emancipation Proclamation or the Civil Rights Act of 1964. She almost didn't mind when the affluent white boys in her school said she was "pretty for a black girl." She almost didn't mind when her teachers called her Tamara or Ta'Shena or Tatiana or any other conventional black girl name. She almost didn't mind being the token black friend in her primarily white peer group, and she almost didn't mind when they constantly bombarded her with questions about race.

"Do you think that all white people are racist?" Becky would ask her as they walked to fourth period chemistry together.

"Will I be cultural appropriating if I wear box braids for my birthday next week?" Mackenzie asked during lunch, combing through her thin bleach-blonde hair, as Tasha tried to finish her broccoli and cheddar soup in peace.

"But if I can't say it, then why is it okay for all the rappers to do so?" Amy would complain to Tasha as they ran laps in gym.

Tasha almost didn't mind any of it until one day, in the spring semester of her senior year, the second black kid to ever arrive at Dalton Prep showed up. Tasha could still remember that day like the palm of her hand. Thomas Jefferson (yes, that was his real name) walked into Tasha's homeroom with an unusually cool gait, as if he had no idea what it meant to exist in a predominantly white world. She couldn't believe his gall when, right after the teacher introduced him to a sea of pale faces, he strode over to the back of the class and slid into his seat. Tasha, who'd spent twelve years sitting in the front row so that her teachers would never assume she was a slacker, almost let out an audible gasp at his bold action.

"Thomas, if you need any help locating your classes, I'm sure Tasha will be more than happy to assist you," Ms. Connors said, gesturing vaguely toward Tasha's desk. Tasha could feel her almond brown cheeks transform into ripe tomatoes. Of course she was assigned as his personal guide for the day. What were the chances of them even having any classes together, with Dalton's 800-count student body?

When the bell for first period rang, however, Tasha was mildly surprised when she turned to her left and saw Thomas, who stood slightly above her forehead, obliviously walking beside her. As they walked through the crowded hallway, full of students shifting their backpacks as they scurried to class, she noticed him occasionally look up from his schedule to locate the room number assigned to him.

"Excuse me?" Thomas lightly tapped her shoulder. Startled, and slightly irritated for a reason she could not yet explain, Tasha turned to face him.

"What?" her tone was harsh, but Thomas didn't react to it.

"Are you Tasha?" he asked. She briskly nodded but failed to meet his gaze completely.

"Do you know where room A65 is?"

Once more, Tasha almost gasped in disbelief. There was no way this kid had the same morning class as her. What were the chances?

"You're not in Honors French, are you?" she asked with a slight edge in her voice. Thomas nodded. Either he didn't notice, or maybe he just didn't care.

"I am, actually."

"It's right around this corner," Tasha said, pointing toward the row of lockers they were about to pass. "You better hurry up, though. Madame Toussaint hates tardiness."

"Noted." Thomas slightly picked up his pace, and together they made their way to room A65—Honors French.

"Bonjour, bonjour," Madame Toussaint said, nodding at Thomas and Tasha as they entered the class. While Tasha slid into her usual seat beside Amy's and Becky's, she watched in amazement as Thomas strolled to the back of the class again.

"Class, we have a new student joining us," Madame Toussaint announced in her usual heavy accent, as if two black kids didn't stick out like fish out of water in a school as white as Dalton. Thomas gave a small wave to the class, and Tasha could feel both Amy's and Becky's eyes glued to his every movement.

"I wonder where he's from," Amy whispered to Becky when Madame Toussaint turned her back and began writing that day's French idioms on the board.

"Probably somewhere in the eastern part of the city, you

know," Becky replied. Tasha rolled her eyes, but cautiously bit her tongue. They knew that the eastern part of the city was where black, mostly lower-class citizens lived. The tuition at Dalton Prep was $26,000 each year, and they weren't known for being generous with their scholarships.

Once Madame Toussaint finished scribbling the French idioms, she looked toward the class and asked for a volunteer to translate them. Olly Kluggenheimer, an eager sophomore, was the first to raise his hand.

"Yes! Olly, please share with us the English translations of these phrases," Madame Toussaint said. Olly tried but failed to properly translate each phrase. Two more students, Rebecca Larson and Fred Stewart, failed as well. Tasha couldn't blame them. Madame Toussaint's idioms were always the worst part of class. It usually took five incorrect interpretations before she finally gave in and translated them to the students herself. Tasha waited patiently for Madame Toussaint to give away the translations when, from the back of the class, she could see Thomas's hand go up in the air from the corner of her eye.

"Yes, Marcus?" Madame Toussaint asked. Thomas cleared his throat.

"It's Thomas, ma'am."

Madame Toussaint blushed in embarrassment. "Ah, yes. My apologies. Do you need something?"

Thomas shook his head. "I would like to translate the phrases."

Tasha watched Madame Toussaint's face transition from misplaced pity to childlike confusion.

"Are you sure you're ready to do so? It's only your first day." She asked.

"I'm sure." Thomas replied. "I was in French Honor Society at my old school."

Madame Toussaint nodded, and one by one, Thomas flawlessly translated the five idioms, to much of the class's and Madame Toussaint's astonishment.

"Wow," Madame Toussaint started. "That was impressive!"

Thomas gazed down at his desk, as if he was deep in thought, and Tasha recognized that look immediately. They never expect much from us, she thought to herself.

At the start of lunch, Tasha walked nervously into the cafeteria, as if it were her first day again and she was searching for a place to fit in. She looked toward her usual table, where Amy and Becky and Mackenzie sat, and almost thought about joining them, but something seemed off. They looked happier, she noted to herself. Their smiles were wider, they laughed much louder, and they seemed to be equally engaged in a conversation Tasha would never understand. She'd never seen them so joyful before and didn't want her presence to disturb it. She gazed over the cafeteria until she spotted a nearly empty table near the window. Only one other person sat at it. As she walked over, Tasha mentally prepared herself for what she should say to Thomas. She debated whether to apologize to him for being a jerk all day but decided comfortable silence would benefit them both. He gave her a friendly nod as she slid into the seat, her lunchbox still unopened. Across from her, Thomas munched absentmindedly on a bag of chips.

"Can we start over?" Tasha asked.

Thomas shrugged. "Why? Did we get off on the wrong foot?"

Tasha could smell the sarcasm in his words, but upon seeing a playful grin appear on his face, she assumed he understood what she meant.

Tasha smiled back, and for the first time in four years, she didn't mind being considered an outcast.

# Evolution

**VICKY BROWN**, Grade 12, Age 17. South Carolina Governor's School for the Arts & Humanities, Greenville, SC. Mamie Morgan, *Educator*

Three hundred thousand years ago
Homo heidelbergensis reached
Iberian hills, found in a pit of bones
deep enough for you to fill with the
museum's collections of porcelain cups,
Civil War uniforms & fragments
of the atomic bomb dropped on Mars Bluff.
You hold my hand through each exhibit,
tell me the Mesozoic reptiles behind glass
aren't real & the wide human skulls, neither
are they. Their chins, like ham croquettes,
set them apart from wild, hairy things,
chimeras or chimpanzees. You ask: How old
is the Earth? Billions. You say twelve thousand.
Maybe we've been put together like faded bouquets
of pelvis fossils & rivulets of gazpacho blood.
In a dream, you left rocks at my doorstep,
the way nineteenth-century men
crawled into tunnels at Atapuerca & made teeth
necklaces for their lovers.
You ask: Where did they go after they died?
Into the pit. Glorified with nothing but
thick skin & chants, chapped lips.

# Ocean Tables

**OSARUGUE OTEBELE**, Grade 12, Age 16. Hollis F. Price Middle College High School, Memphis, TN. Chandra Boddie and Diana Gentry, *Educators*

I don't know where all of me is
I know it is not here
I know it is tucked away in letters I write to brothers and
sisters I will never meet
We were made orphans by the slave trade
I know it whispers in metaphors
I know it is in pots, engraved with ancient languages.
Parts of me. Still make ocean home
Still wake up from nightmares and can taste salt water
Still wander through underground passageways
I know my mother tongue but I wonder if
My mother knows, her mothers, mothers tongue
Sang negro spirituals?
We have missed hundreds of funerals
I wonder if there are gaps the size of slave ships where my
ancestors should be
Wonder if they know that I mourned their loss
That I write obituaries and struggle with which language I
should start with
I don't know where all of me is
My pangea broke up more than 300 hundred years ago
They should know where the rest of me is.
On my family tree are fallen leaves
On my family tree are strange fruit
On my family tree

**GRACE BALDWIN**, *Ladder*, Drawing & Illustration. Grade 12, Age 18,
Episcopal High School, Alexandria, VA. Frank Phillips, *Educator*

# SPECIAL ACHIEVEMENT AND AMERICAN VOICES AWARDS

Dedicated and generous supporters make it possible for us to provide additional recognition and scholarships. In 2018, we were pleased to add a new opportunity—the Civic Expression Award, in partnership with the Campaign for the Civic Mission of Schools supported by the Maurice R. Robinson Fund. We were also grateful to continue the New York Life Award, sponsored by the New York Life Foundation; The Herblock Award for Editorial Cartoon, sponsored by The Herb Block Foundation; and the Best-in-Grade Awards, sponsored by Bloomberg Philanthropies.

In addition, we were pleased to present the American Voices Award, the highest regional honor that is presented to one writer from each region. Works that most exemplify originality, technical skill, and the emergence of a personal voice receive this Award.

Selections of these awarded writing works are included in the following pages.

Some of the writing selections have been excerpted. Visit **artandwriting.org/galleries** to read all of the work as it was submitted.

# Origin Story

**SOPHIE PAQUETTE**, Grade 11, Age 15. Interlochen Arts Academy, Interlochen, MI. Mika Perrine and Joe Sacksteder, *Educators;* American Voices Award

Every afternoon, the school bus drops the four of us off at the old 7-Eleven behind Marsha's house. We stumble through the door in the same humming clump, bell chiming overhead. The register boy looks up, all snaggle-toothed, lip hitched where the white edge of a molar pokes out. Elsie smiles and waves at the security camera, exposing the pink of her palm like something secret. (Elsie's always got an audience.) Here, we know the aisles like we know the nooks of our own bodies. Marsha slides a finger down the crinkling rows of candy wrappers, June tucks bags of chips in her lap, pinches the corners until all that's left inside is dust. Elsie spins, spins, spins the sunglasses stand on its axis. (We think she could spin the whole world like that if she wanted to, flicking the tip of her finger.) We've missed so many family dinners. At night in the 7-Eleven, flies cling to the caged light bulb. Moths rustle and flit. We watch our bodies swell through the hemispherical mirrors hung in the corners, measure our stretching spines by the numbered notches on the door. Grow out of our clothes and change into truck-stop

T-shirts and cargo shorts. Elsie ties her shirt just beneath her bra, black wire visible, creamy slice of stomach. She wraps a loop of Slim Jims around her waist and counts how many it takes to circle back to her bellybutton. She holds the rope out to the rest of us, makes us count too. "It only takes you three?" she asks June, eyes hidden behind old '70s shades, the circular kind. June just nods. "That's bullshit," says Elsie. "Measure again." Elsie is the first to start swearing; she calls us all "slut" or "whore" and pretends not to see when June pulls three Slim Jims around the flat of her tummy and lies, "You're right, Elsie. It takes four. You are smallest." Marsha buys a box of tampons, pays all in quarters and dimes, change clattering to the counter. Even the snaggle-toothed boy's scaly skin goes a warm shade of strawberry Starburst when we ask for the bathroom key. (It's tied to a crumbling brick.) Huddled in the single-stalled handicap toilet, Elsie unrolls the instructions, shows us where everything goes, everything, not just the tampon. Our giggles echo in the vents like the sound a box of Tic Tacs makes, all shaken up. No one is surprised when Elsie is the first to bring a boy back to the 7-Eleven, that same stall. Ears pressed against the door, we listen to the scratch of their sneakers on the tile. Later, she shows us how to slip a coin into what we all thought was a candy machine, rusty on the bathroom wall. "Candy?" she cackles. "You dumb sluts! You Virgin Marys!" She's the first of us to lean in real close to the snaggle-toothed boy (a man now—adult braces are a bitch) and touch the glint of his molar, that tip of her finger. June sits in the corner and crunches her chips. Elsie pokes the bulge of baby soft squishing out of June's hips and cackles her smoky cackle, says, "Let's see how many Slim Jims it takes now, June Bug. June Beetle. Junie B. Jones." Elsie's skin stains yellow like the tiles, or the tiles stain the color of her skin. Our voices melt into the sound a straw makes, scraping the bottom of a styrofoam cup, and Elsie tries on so many sunglasses that we forget what her real eyes look like. We grow past the notches on the door, the hemispherical mirrors crack. (Elsie's still waving at the camera, smiling to all her fans.) A procession of boys parades through the 7-Eleven, and each time, the snaggle-toothed man slaps the brick onto the counter. We press our ears to the handicap stall door. Soon, snaggle-toothed man begets snaggle-toothed boy, and it is this new child who replaces his father at the register, who scoops Marsha's quarters and dimes into his smarmy palm. When he comes of age, Elsie pulls him into the stall and deflowers him, devours him, snaggle and all. We watch Elsie's belly swell (it takes five, ten, twenty Slim Jims now), stretching veins like licorice unstrung. June chews her chips. Marsha counts her coins. The baby is born into the handicap toilet with Mountain Dew hair and gummy worm lips, face wrinkled in Red Hot sob. Elsie swaddles her in a crinkly bag, Thank You Have a Nice Day, and tucks the plastic with a safety pin. Child latched and pruny on her chest, Elsie walks out the door—bell chiming behind her, security camera tracing the swish and swivel of those hips as they recede from the screen.

# Shaving Cream

**VICTORIA GONG**, Grade 11, Age 16. Mississippi School of Math & Science, Columbus, MS. Emma Richardson, *Educator*; American Voices Award

In the morning I watch Baba's slow limp to the bathroom. Both he and the door creak as he heaves it open, and he stumbles as his foot catches on the lip of the threshold.

I go to the window and yank at the blinds. They catch on their rusty hinges and hang stubbornly, half-drawn. Stark sunlight crawls into the room, but it seems too weary to reach into the far corners. Shadows roil in the deep creases of the sheets rumpled on the hospital bed. I notice, not for the first time, that there are whorls of fingerprints and strands of hair trapped in the plastered walls. The stench of ammonia lances up my forehead, and I pinch at the bridge of my nose until the headache reduces to a dull thrum between my eyes; smells in the hospital room come in waves like the patients, crumbling away without notice, then returning with different names and faces and unchanging symptoms—old age, failing organs, persistent melanoma.

Turning, I remember that the nurse said to me yesterday to check on Baba more often, so I tap on the bathroom door with two knuckles. Then, I remind myself he's hard of hearing, so I call out, "Baba?"

There's no reply.

I push the door open anyway and find Baba standing at the sink, his eyes purple and baggy, his cheeks covered in shaving cream. He turns the faucet on and lets the water run until it's warm. His nose dangles like a lump of melting candle wax when he hunkers over.

I watch him tremble as he shaves stroke by stroke, the razor rasping from his cheekbone to his gulping Adam's apple. Baba nicks himself a few times, but he doesn't bother to rinse the cuts. His blood turns the shaving cream pink, like the frosting on a birthday cake.

Baba's gaze wanders once he's halfway done, drops from the mirror to the counter of the sink, where there's a paper cup with two toothbrushes, a tube of travel-size toothpaste, a bar of soap, and the old picture frame. The frame is three by four, the size of Baba's heart, and it holds a grainy photo of him and my mother on their third wedding anniversary. I'm not yet born, and they hold champagne glasses, laughing. My mother, dressed in royal blue, has her pinky finger sticking out.

Baba picks up the photograph, and I watch in the mirror as the blue films around his irises seem to expand, as if he's aging before my eyes. I'm not sure how long he stands over the sink, gripping the picture in his left hand and his razor in the right, looking like a retiring Santa Claus with his half-beard of shaving cream, but when I step forward and tug the razor from his hand, it falls away without protest.

"The nurse will be around soon, Baba," I say, shaving his other cheek clean. "You'll want to be ready."

The photograph lays flat in both of his palms. He does not cry, and he carries it back to his bed.

# Three Shots Through the Window of a Synagogue in Indiana

**DANIEL BLOKH**, Grade 11, Age 16. Alabama School of Fine Arts, Birmingham, AL. TJ Beitelman, Ashley Jones, and Kwoya Maples, *Educators*; Best-in-Grade Award

Every bullet was aimed for sky.
The thin white one carrying my father and mother happened
to be interrupted by another home, a different country.
Here, no one would be turned away. Here
every synagogue was more than a path
to exit wound.
Every bullet aimed for the sky.
A bullet does not know it is a bullet
until blood. A year is not a year until
it is emptied. My mother and father stand over a TV
and remember. Wring their hands.
I look out at the sky that brought them here, riddled
with bright tunnels.
Every bullet is aimed for this sky.
Some are interrupted. Some miss.

# Six Definitions for American

**EILEEN HUANG**, Grade 12, Age 18. High Technology High School, Lincroft, NJ. Alan Brown and Sarah Gross, *Educators*; Silver Medal with Distinction

American
1. *(adj.) relating to or characteristic of the United States or its inhabitants*
 or relating to mistaking silence
    for patriotism / or characteristic of barbecue
            and backyard and
        basement and bb gun / the thrill
      you get  when you pull the trigger
            here  and watch a dead thing become
                a dead thing over  there


2. *(adj.) relating to or denoting the continents of America* we
have taken
 this three-syllable word  and made it fit our  naked tongues /
have taken it from  those here before us / before we clothed
 ourselves in united    before we sprayed them
            with water cannon and shoved their heads
      to the ground / shoved their heads /
                to the ground


3. *(noun) the English language as it is used in the United States;
American English* / and
   the lady in the supermarket yells at my mother to *speak*

    *American* / my mother
who says *smoothie* like *smooshie* and doesn't know
she from he sometimes / we shop for a knife to cut / off our
mother
        tongue / and i want to buy a new  identity
       and i think writing poems
      about my other-
    ness will somehow dissolve this  skin / my parents
    didn't know what
   middle names were /  when they came here
    so there's a gap between
      my first and last / an ocean that divides
       country from  no country


4. *(noun) a native or citizen of the United States*
    and native falls
     from my closed mouth
  like the Mandarin that I have learned
    to forget / the language that lies
  limp and bloodied in my mouth / the Chinese characters
   in my name that I have forgotten how to write / and do
you know /
    what it's like / to forget /  your name? / it's like
  when we first put pen
 to paper  and marked this land as ours / this empty
    cathedral / as ours /
like when we stopped saying
    *We the people*
   and learned to say  *those people* / those people
   whom we have left  childless
  those mothers we have left with empty backyard
   and full
      graveyard

5. *related phrases: "As American as apple pie"* / mother, don't
you know that this is America? /
    they have made me
       *American* / i have a middle name now and it is / *chink*
    they've taken flowers from graves
        babies from mothers
          they took Tamir from his  boyhood /
  and trust me / i've looked for it / when he lost it  i tried
digging in earth with / dirt-
      filled nails to find it
    and found only
      a handful of dried flies  that once sang
         wasn't he American?
        and wasn't he American? / aren't we
         American?


6. *to be American is to hold your anger in your throat like
misfire* /
      and mother, I've stopped saying the pledge at school
  because I can't find any / allegiance
    to this country / that names us   dead things
    before we speak / because our bodies lie under
     godless night skies /
    because what is the flag but a fleeting thing without a
     heart-/
       beat / but mother,
   I know how to / speak American now / and I know
    that here / a bullet
      is just our way of saying  *goodbye.*

# The Lunatic (A Pantoum)

**NOAH TREVINO**, Grade 9, Age 14. Howard W. Blake High School, Tampa, FL. Casey Curry, *Educator*; Best-in-Grade Award

All you can smell is the breath of the lunatic.
Their shouts flood my room, ruining our lullabies.
Mother tries her best but can't contain the beast.
Their river of beer swept away our love.

Their shouts flood my room, ruining our lullabies.
I watch the film of your aggression every night.
Their river of beer swept away our love.
They created a realm of horror for their loved ones.

I watch the film of your aggression every night.
Drip. Drip. The rain came after the divorce.
They created a realm of horror for their loved ones.
Each day appears a new bottle in the kitchen.

Drip. Drip. The rain came after the divorce.
Who will protect us when the Goddess Tara herself won't?
Each day appears a new bottle in the kitchen.
Our sacred sanctuary will never be the same.

Who will protect us when the Goddess Tara herself won't?
Mother tries her best but can't contain the beast.
Our family's sanctuary will never be the same.
All you can smell is the breath of the lunatic.

# Terrorist

**NEELAM BOHRA**, Grade 12, Age 18, McKinney High School,
McKinney, TX. Alyssa Boehringer, *Educator;* Silver Medal
with Distinction

"He's just a terrorist." My parents laughed.

I flinched. At our dinner table, with one phrase, they had
robed my best friend in a vest of bombs. With a simple word,
they had declared his dedication to Islam one of blood-dipped
hate, his whole religion guilty of a feud between my Indian,
Hindu parents and Pakistan. Yet all my knowledge of his com-
passion for others, his timid personality and kind words, did
not come to my mouth. Instead, I didn't say anything.

The next day at school, I heard it again:

"Terrorist."

His eyes pushed me to my feet until he turned back around
to finish the Pledge of Allegiance. We weren't friends, but we
weren't enemies either—did he really just call me a terrorist? I
didn't even mean to stay seated as I arranged papers. I didn't
think my bent knees qualified as an act of terror. But still, I
didn't say anything.

The word bounced around in my head, but I couldn't feel its
full impact.

I am brown. I am proud. And my silence caused humiliation to grow deep inside of me. Why couldn't I express the sadness, the indignation?

It was just a joke. It was just a joke. It was just a joke.

But it wasn't a joke.

I wanted to keep the peace, hold back from creating a scene, and pay the immigrant's price for freedom like my parents, and my grandparents, who I had watched politely tolerate racism. Other immigrants faced harder situations every day, and maybe speaking out would trivialize their struggles—it was just a word, anyway.

Yet part of me wanted to speak out, to scream. My culture is not just some piece of luggage for airport security to search. My parents did not tirelessly work night shifts at gas stations while attending full-time college, did not face life at 18 alone, did not relentlessly pursue their one-way ticket to America for it to become an inescapable nametag of discrimination and hatred. As I fought myself internally, though, I couldn't outwardly fight the word. And the will to stay calm consumed my resentment.

When I sat down for dinner with my parents that night, I finally opened my mouth. I shared with them how a boy I'd known since fourth grade had called me a terrorist, the very word they'd used the night before. I could see the outrage in their eyes. But I didn't let them speak—not yet. I reminded them how their anger was justified, yet hypocritical. I told them how they had condemned another culture to the same fate I had faced. Their infuriated looks froze with silence. I had won an inch of space within their minds; maybe the old conflict could be slowly chipped away. Speaking out gave me peace and made me realize the importance of expression.

Since those events, the word *terrorist* means something new to me. It means the persecution people carried out in the Middle East. But it also means the racism people with brown skin faced in America, regardless of religion. It represents pure discrimination. It means the intolerance of my own parents, people I loved, people facing the same intolerance themselves.

I can't imagine what "terrorist" means to victims of actual terrorism. But this experience makes me want to try. I want to tell the stories of victims of terrorism's violence, so their cries don't drown between the words of a "joke" told behind the lush grasses of suburbia. I want to illustrate their struggles, so the world may care enough to reach out and help. In following my dream to be a journalist, in writing and reporting, I could combat hate rather than revive it.

Now the word *terrorist* no longer stings my ears. Its sound has become a challenge, a battle cry, for those oppressed in its name. And I am ready to fight.

# The Hope for the Best

**ELISEO CORONA**, Grade 10, Age Unknown. South Elgin High School, Elgin, IL. Brittany Hennessey, *Educator*; Best-in-Grade Award

### Characters
CHARACTER 1: AMBER ROSEANNE—21-year-old female, "lone wolf" attitude, casual bad-girl look, SHAY MICHAEL's friend, strong and independent.
CHARACTER 2: SHAY MICHAELS—22-year-old male, awkward social skills, has secret feelings toward AMBER, reliable and good listener.

### Setting
[It is present day in the nighttime. There's a backdrop of stars and a few trees on the sides. There's a truck placed on center stage, facing the audience, on an angle to the right. Rocks of different shapes and sizes surround the car from right center, left center, and a few on down center stage (and surrounding areas).]

### Scene 1
[The lights are dim, except for a spotlight shining on AMBER and SHAY. It's chilly, so SHAY and AMBER are wearing sweaters. AMBER has a leather jacket, a nice lace shirt, jeans,

and combat boots. SHAY has a gray zip-up sweater with a
polo underneath, jeans, and a pair of running shoes. They are
sitting on the hood of the truck. AMBER has her feet crossed,
SHAY has his feet dangling off the front. AMBER has a bottle
of hard cider while SHAY has a flask. AMBER is sitting on the
left side of the hood, while SHAY sits on the right side.]

AMBER
Heaven is for suckers.
(Takes a drink and lets out a light grunt. Looks at the bottle
for a second before looking up.)
SHAY
What do you mean?
AMBER
Who needs it?
(Shrugs loosely and focuses stare on SHAY)
I mean, you work your ass off trying to stay pure and clean,
and when you get there, all you get is pampering.
SHAY
Isn't that the point? To reward the "saints" for their good
lives on Earth?
(Raises hands in pseudo-preach. Both laugh. Shay uncaps
flask and takes a drink, coffee spilling out onto his pants.)
AMBER
(Giggles slightly)
What is it this time? Dark roast? French vanilla? Decaf?
SHAY
(Wiping off his pants with his free hand)
Uh . . . yeah, d-dark.
AMBER
(Smiling and looking at the stars, slowly looking more medi-
tative)

[Beat]

Those . . . bastards . . . they just leave you down here to fend for yourself while they have little . . . tea parties upstairs.

(Takes a drink)

SHAY

Uh-huh. Okay. So . . . you hate Heaven because you know you have to work for it?

AMBER

(Stares at the audience)

It's more like because you know you can't get it. Eh, this life, well, you know it can't last. But it all seems so good with so many "evil" temptations, that you fall into it, you know? Y-you start falling in love with life. We know that there is something greater, er, at least some people think it, but the journey is too lonely and too hard, that you end up straying away.

(Looks at the ground)

That's one part of it anyway.

(Turns to look at SHAY and drinks)

[Beat]

SHAY

What's the other part?

AMBER

(Smiles a wide, sly smile)

Damn, Shay, you're a curious one.

SHAY

(Smiles embarrassedly, trying to slightly hide his face)

AMBER

(Faking exasperation)

But fine! I'll tell you, I guess. Otherwise, I think I'd blow up with all these thoughts in my head.

[Beat]

Heaven sounds like a place full of hypocrites. You work so hard to get there and then forget the point of it all. The journey is just as important, if not more, than the destination. That's the first thing everyone should know. Living here, I mean, living overall, builds you up, you know? It gives you a personality, an identity that you hold on to with your life for the rest of your life. It makes you the person you are.

Some people are fine with themselves, but there are also those who want to start over and be a new person.

(Takes a long swig of cider and closes eyes)

[Beat]

And I'm good with who I am.

(Opens eyes)

SHAY

(Looks at AMBER wide-eyed, surprised at her last statement)

(For AMBER dialogue, SHAY looks at AMBER intently the whole time.)

AMBER

(Lets out a sigh)

I've been through a lot of things, you know? I-I-I-I've lost people. Sure, I've met a few others, and some are not the kind of people you'd want to meet, but that's just fine with me. I am me because of everything, and I've let it go. I got over it a long time ago.

[Beat]

I don't let it affect me, but I think it still matters. I don't think about it, but I keep it inside of me. It's my past and I know that is important. Heaven . . .

(Looks at SHAY)

Well, Heaven is forgetting. They spoil you and treat you like royalty until that's what you feel like. You throw away your old life and embrace the one in which you are what you want to be.

(Looks down and makes any emphasising hand motion at next part)

But that's not right. The struggles and injustices and aches and pains are all key things to teach us lessons.

(Counts off with fingers)

Number one: Be humble. Number two: Always move on. Number three: Life. Isn't. Fair.

(Puts hands at sides and breathes out heavily. Closes eyes.)

Heaven gives people the power to ignore and demolish these rules. You get riches, and you can sit on your little ass and be fed and life is what you want it to be. You cling to this new life, if you can even call it that, and you let go of the last one until you start losing yourself.

(Opens eyes)

Your personality crumbles, and your identity is destroyed. Why? Because you can't remember what it's like to hurt or to cry or to just feel bad. Everything you are or once were disappears, and you're okay with this because you keep looking ahead, as people always do.

(Mimes shooting by placing hand on flat palm and moving up at next part)

But also, like people, you don't . . . look . . . far enough.

(Lets hands and stare fall down)

You look into the near future and let the rest figure itself on its own. You pretend to be a fatalist and let it slide until you become nothing. It's times like these where it's okay to look back, you know?

(Looks at SHAY)

Where it's actually necessary and fundamental, where it helps you fight to remain the person you were when you stepped through the god-forsaken gates.

(Shakes head)

But people never do that.

(Wipes away tears)

They just think of what could be until you become a soul
without a spirit, and happiness becomes an illusion that helps
you get through.

[Beat]

You turn into nothing, along with everyone else and you live
that way forever. Without any hope, or sense for the need of
hope, to be saved from Salvation.

SHAY

(Looks down, hands on forelegs, as if bracing self for support)

[Long break, about 10 seconds]

(Pulls out wooden cross from pocket opposite of AMBER.
Looks at it silently, slightly holding it toward audience,
following the silhouette, then stashing it away hurriedly.)

Well, uh—we . . . uh, we should get going.

AMBER

(Wipes tears and sniffles while getting off the hood and getting
into the passenger seat of the car, looking down the whole
time)

SHAY

(Jumps off of car nervously. Walks toward the driver's seat of
the car and turns it on.)

Dammit . . .

[Curtains close as sound of engine comes on]

# Defrauding or Discriminating: The Constitutionality of Voter Identification Laws in the 21st Century

**NATHAN ZHAO**, Grade 11, Age 16. Wayland High School, Wayland, MA.
Patricia Halpin, *Educator*; Civic Expression Award

"Unless the right to vote be secure and undenied, all other rights are insecure and subject to denial for all our citizens. The challenge to this right is a challenge to America itself."

—President Lyndon B. Johnson

Eleven percent of U.S. citizens, or more than 21 million Americans, do not have government-issued photo identification that is required for voting in some states.[2] These states require registered voters to show a specified form of identification, sometimes photo identification, in order to exercise their constitutional right to vote. The Fourteenth Amendment states, "No state shall make or enforce any law which shall abridge the privileges or immunities of citizens of the United States." The constitution also defines voting as such a right of U.S. citizens.

Moreover, the Voting Rights Act of 1965, a landmark piece of federal legislation, states that "No voting qualification or prerequisite to voting, or standard, practice, or procedure shall be imposed or applied by any State or political subdivision to deny or abridge the right of any citizen of the United States to vote on account of race or color." Although the Supreme Court has upheld photo voter ID laws in the past, these voting laws are unconstitutional under the Fourteenth Amendment and the Voting Rights Act of 1965.

Prerequisites to vote at the polls have a history in America and are rooted in discriminatory practices. After black males became enfranchised through the Fifteenth Amendment's ratification in 1870, former Confederate states, almost all Democrat, needed to ensure their control of state government.[3] As African-Americans overwhelmingly supported the Republican party at the time, Democrats needed to institute permanent barriers to the group's vote. Thus, Southern Democrats created the first suffrage qualifications: "literacy, residence, and the payment of taxes."[4] Known collectively as the "Jim Crow" voting laws, they were designed to make it systematically difficult for African-Americans to vote; a high percentage of African-Americans were illiterate, lacked an "approved" residence, or did not have the financial means to pay the "poll tax." Poor white people were allowed to pass by these rules under "grandfather" or "understanding" clauses, exceptions not extended to African-Americans.[5] The practice of presenting some sort of an ID at polls began in South Carolina in the 1950s.[6] These were also racially charged, as it was much more difficult for African-Americans to obtain such an ID than for white people because of discrimination by state workers providing IDs. In combination, these laws proved effective; Democrats ruled the South in a one-party system until the Civil Rights Movement.

However, as early as the 1940s, fundamental reform occurred in the national Democratic party. Liberal "New Deal" Democrats and President Franklin Roosevelt now controlled the party's platform. After the Great Depression and World War II, Roosevelt implemented a plethora of social welfare programs aimed at helping the poorest Americans. As these programs benefited many African-Americans, who were poorer than whites, the former began to vote Democrat.[7]

The poll tax's repeal and President Lyndon B. Johnson's signing of the 1965 Voting Rights Act were also major political blows to the discriminatory voting policies in the South.[8] Southern conservatives fled the Democratic Party for the Republican Party; meanwhile, white liberals were drawn to the former under Johnson. Between 1970 and 2000, attention to voter suppression laws diminished. While several states still passed voluntary ID laws, all still allowed voters to cast a ballot even if they did not have the requested ID. By 2000, fourteen states (some Republican, others Democrat) had some sort of an ID law.[9] That year, the competitive Bush/Gore election led to increased attention to voter ID laws.

After that election, voter ID laws became a partisan issue. Many states with Republican legislatures passed voter ID laws; proponents of these laws claimed they were instituted to stop voter fraud and voter impersonation. The Heritage Foundation, a conservative think tank, argued that the primary purpose of voter ID laws was to prevent in-person voter fraud.[10] This turned into the main argument of the Republican Party in favor of these laws. Moreover, the 2005 Commission on Federal Election Reform's bipartisan recommendation for voter identification at the polls stirred more states, mostly GOP-leaning, to adopt voter ID laws at an ever-increasing pace.[11] However, in reality, conservative Republicans' primary motive for the laws were not to stop voter fraud; rather, they wanted these laws to stop those unable to obtain an ID, mostly Democrats, from voting.

Voter ID laws have been repeatedly challenged in both national and state courts. Soon after the Commission's 2005 recommendation, Georgia and Indiana pioneered a new, "strict" form of voter ID. Instead of requesting an ID, these states required a photo ID to be presented on election day in order to vote. The law was upheld by the U.S. Supreme Court in *Crawford* v. *Marion County* (6-3) in April 2008. This paved the way for the accelerated adoption of photo ID laws by state legislatures from 2011 to 2013.

In *Shelby County* v. *Holder* (2013), the Supreme Court found (5-4) that section 4b of the Voting Rights Act of 1965 was unconstitutional. It contained a "preclearance" measure that required certain states and local governments (as determined by a formula) to obtain a determination by the United States Attorney General as to whether their law was discriminatory against the Fifteenth Amendment. Since the state and local governments that fell under the formula's region were freed from the preclearance mandate, Republican legislatures in 17 states adopted new laws, and courts allowed these to stay in place for the 2014 midyear elections.

However, in July 2016, the 5th U.S. Circuit Court of Appeals, which is generally regarded as conservative, struck down Texas's voter ID law in a 9-6 vote, saying it violated the Voting Rights Act. The law required one out of seven forms of photo ID, allowing handgun licenses but not college student IDs. Interestingly, Hispanic people were two times and black people three times as likely to lack an acceptable ID under the law. [12] In January 2017, the Supreme Court rejected an appeal from Texas on the grounds that it was still being decided by a lower state court. However, the case is still likely to be heard by the Supreme Court in the future.[13]

In North Carolina on July 29, 2016, a three-judge panel of the 4th U.S. Circuit Court of Appeals unanimously struck down the state's voter ID requirements and numerous other provisions that the court said were enacted with the intent of making it harder for minorities to vote. The court wrote that these changes to the voting process "target[ed] African-Americans with almost surgical precision."[14] Furthermore, in August 2016, a U.S. District Court struck down several parts of Wisconsin's strict voter ID law passed by the state's Republican-controlled legislature, ruling that it was discriminatory. However, this ruling was overturned by the 7th Circuit Court of Appeals, and voters were required to present photo IDs in the 2016 election.[15]

Voter ID laws have resulted in voter suppression and lower turnouts. A 2014 U.S. Government Accountability Office study analyzed the 2012 presidential election in Kansas and Tennessee. It found that ID laws reduced voter turnout by 1.9 percentage points in Kansas and 2.2 percentage points in Tennessee, translating into a total of 122,000 votes lost in between the two states.[17] More important, the study found that voter turnout in two groups, African-Americans and voters under 25, dropped disproportionately in 2012. Since these two groups largely vote Democrat, the Republican Party benefited. Although this lack of turnout did not change the course of the election on its own, it, combined with other factors, such as voter intimidation, strategic polling place hours, and complete closing of polling places, could have shifted the tide of the election.

Voter ID laws also significantly impacted the 2016 presidential election. This election was the first in 50 years without the full protection of the 1965 Voting Rights Act, due to strict voter ID laws.[18] The effects were seen in Wisconsin, where Trump won the state for the Republican Party for the first time since 1988. Turnout plummeted to the lowest point in 20 years.[19] Trump won the state by just over 27,000 votes, and according to the state's own records, as many as 300,000 people may have been disenfranchised because they lacked a proper photo ID.[20] Neil Albrecht, the executive director of Wisconsin's Election Commission, noted that declines in voting were greatest in high-poverty and traditionally "blue" regions, where lack of IDs was most common and that Clinton desperately needed to win.[21] Albrecht said that he believed that a lack of IDs is what caused this decline in voting in "blue" counties that Clinton needed to secure to win the state.

Albrecht added that his office received a flood of calls from voters in the county's poorest districts who said they were unable to cast a ballot because they lacked the proper identification. Although only 600 ballots were thrown away because voters did not have the right ID, Albrecht said he worries many more did not even attempt to vote because of the photo ID law. [22] Had those citizens in these traditionally "blue" regions been able to vote, Clinton would have easily won the state.

In many states, including Texas, North Carolina, Indiana, North Dakota, and Arkansas, stringent photo ID laws were all ruled unconstitutional by either a state court or a U.S. District Court of Appeals before the November election. However, not all voters got this message, and more importantly, neither did local election officials. In conservative states, it is believed that some of these officials told voters that they needed ID, despite such laws having been overturned by courts. Because of the law's unclear status, many of these officials were able to successfully prevent legal, registered voters from voting. Sherrilyn Ifill, president of the NAACP Legal Defense and Educational

Fund, said that "voters were confused because of changes to their polling places and a lack of accurate information provided to them by their state officials."[23] This not only discouraged voters but also resulted in unlawful enforcement of ID laws. In Michigan, Electionland received multiple reports of poll workers wrongly telling voters they needed an ID to vote, even though the state did not have a voter ID law.[24] Although it is not clear how many voters this false information affected, it is clear that it impacted voter turnout. Furthermore, Nicole Austin-Hillery, director of the Washington, D.C., office of the Brennan Center for Justice, said she was concerned that this unclear nature of voter ID laws may have had a "chilling effect" on voters showing up at the polls.[25] That is, some voters had the false impression that voter ID laws were in place, and, lacking proper ID, they did not attempt to vote.

Photo ID laws are unconstitutional because they violate both the Fourteenth Amendment and the 1965 Voting Rights Act. The Fourteenth Amendment states, "No state shall make or enforce any law which shall abridge the privileges or immunities of citizens of the United States." The right to vote is a constitutionally guaranteed right of citizens of the United States, and voter ID laws discourage and in some cases disallow completely this basic right to people who cannot afford or obtain a voter ID. In reality, 11% of U.S. citizens, or more than 21 million Americans, do not have a government-issued photo ID. Obtaining an ID costs money; even if the ID itself is offered for free, voters are responsible for numerous costs to apply for a government-issued ID. In reality, the combined cost for document fees, travel expenses, and waiting time are estimated to range from $75 to $175, depending on the state. [26] This is unfair to impoverished or low-income Americans who cannot afford such costs. Moreover, the travel or time required to acquire such an ID is often a major burden on people with disabilities, the elderly, or those in rural areas without access to a car or public transportation. In Texas, where the law was "weakened" but not removed, some voters in rural areas had to travel 170 miles to reach the nearest ID office. [27] The significant costs associated with obtaining an ID are unconstitutional, as they abridge the privilege to vote for low-income citizens who cannot afford expensive means to obtain an ID.

Photo ID laws also violate the 1965 Voting Rights Act. Although sections 4b and 5 were effectively removed from the act in *Shelby* v. *Holder* (June 2013), the main clause in section 2 is still in effect: "No voting qualification or prerequisite to voting, or standard, practice, or procedure shall be imposed or applied by any State or political subdivision to deny or abridge the right of any citizen of the United States to vote on account of race or color." However, the laws unfairly target minorities. Nationally, up to 25% of African-American citizens of voting age lack government-issued photo ID, compared with only 8% of white people.[28] North Carolina rejected public assistance and state employee photo IDs as valid for voting. These are disproportionately held by African-Americans. In Texas, concealed weapons permits but not student ID cards are acceptable. Even though both IDs are authentic and legitimate, merely 15% of concealed weapon permit holders are minorities[29] while 55% of students at University of Texas at Austin, a major university in the state, are minorities.[30] All in all, a state court found that about 608,000 registered voters in Texas lacked an acceptable ID and that a disproportionate number of these voters were black or Hispanic.[31] Furthermore, voter ID laws are often enforced in a discriminatory manner. A 2016 Caltech/MIT study found that minority voters are more frequently questioned about ID than are white voters.[32] This means that some white people who do not have ID may still vote due to racial discrimination at polling places. It is evident that voter ID laws unfairly target these minorities and thus violate the 1965 Voting Rights Act by denying and abridging their vote based on race.

The first impact is reduced turnout for minority voters. Several studies have found that photo ID laws have a particularly depressive effect on turnout among racial minorities and other vulnerable groups, worsening the participation gap between voters of color and whites. This is supported by the results of the 2016 election, where turnout for minority voting groups in states like Wisconsin decreased drastically as a result of the implementation of its photo ID law. Furthermore, a recent comprehensive voter ID study conducted by political scientists at the University of California San Diego analyzed turnout in elections between 2008 and 2012. It found "substantial drops in turnout for minorities under strict voter ID laws."[33]

Voter ID laws are a political ploy by Republicans. The laws do not accomplish their stated purpose of fixing "voter fraud"; in fact, in-person fraud is rare. A recent study found that over 1 billion ballots have been cast since 2000. Of those, there were only 28 credible allegations of voter impersonation, the only type of fraud that photo IDs could possibly prevent.[34] Furthermore, election experts say that even when voter fraud happens, it happens more often through mail-in, absentee ballots than people impersonating eligible voters at the polls.[35] Only 6 out of 31 ID states extend their photo ID requirement to absentee voters, who are generally older white people. Of those 28 cases of voter fraud, 14 percent involved absentee ballots, and only 3.6 percent involved voter impersonation.[36] This shows that even voter ID laws cannot stop Republican claims of voter fraud.

Thomas Jefferson wrote in the Declaration of Independence that "all men are created equal." However, the reality is quite different. Mechanisms like voter ID laws discriminate against minorities, denying them the basic right to vote. Beyond the 2016 presidential election, state voter ID laws and the constant challenge to such litigation will continue to have a profound impact on elections in the future; the congressional elections in 2018 and the presidential election in 2020 will again test the legal strength of the laws in court. The Supreme Court is slated in 2018 to hear their first voter ID law case in five years, possibly resulting in a landmark decision that will impact the status of photo ID laws for years. Neil Gorsuch, the Trump-nominated newest justice of the Supreme Court, although he has not heard a voter ID law case in the past, is strongly conservative and will most likely vote in favor of the laws, much like his conservative-leaning colleagues on the court. Gorsuch's recent confirmation will likely be a barrier for voting rights groups as they try to win a future Supreme Court case on the issue. No matter which side the court takes, the battle over voter ID laws is far from over.

In America, a vote is not simply a ballot for a preferred candidate. Rather, it is a symbol of our ideals as a nation and the distinct power of the people to elect their representatives in government. By taking away the vote of minorities, America discards not only their voice in its government, but also the country's promises to these Americans of life, liberty, and the pursuit of happiness.

# The Mourning Of

**KENDALL VORHIS**, Grade 11, Age 17. Goose Creek High School, Goose Creek, SC. Nicholas Geary, *Educator;* New York Life Award

The sun rose that morning, as it always did.
Autumn sunlight parted through the
living room blinds, casting vertical
shadows upon your sunken cheeks,
highlighting every wrinkle, every
blemish I so hastily tried to memorize
before they faded like your lasting
breath.

They told me you were at peace,
but your barren, half-lidded
eyes would not shut no matter
how many desperate attempts I
made to close them, for they did not want
to pretend to be asleep—but taunt me
as I pathetically clutched your
rigid hands to my hollow chest.

Your lax jaw hung open, mouth
paused in an eternal gasp for air that
would never be fulfilled.
If this was peace, unrest was a bitter
punishment for the damned.

Saturated and lively,
Autumn sunlight parted through the
living room blinds, and though you
did not rise to greet its mourning debut,
the sun rose.

**ANGEL LIN**, *See You Soon*, Drawing & Illustration. Grade 10, Age 15, Douglas Anderson School of Arts, Jacksonville, FL. Hillary Hogue, *Educator*

## GOLD AND SILVER AWARDS

Students in grades 7–12 may submit works in eleven writing categories. This year, more than 3,900 writing submissions that were awarded Gold Keys at the regional level were then adjudicated at the national level by authors, educators, and literary professionals. Gold and Silver Medals were awarded to works of writing that demonstrated originality, technical skill, and emergence of a personal voice.

Some of the writing selections have been excerpted.
Visit **artandwriting.org/galleries** to read all of the work as it was submitted.

# Ten

CATARINA CHUNG, Grade 11, Age 17. Bergen County Academies, Hackensack, NJ. Richard Weems, *Educator*

There's Eight, crouched near the smoke hole where the scent of freshly blackened fish always filtered in strong and steady. He was up to his ankles in ashes, the fine dust caked in his ratty old flannel and ripped-up jeans. The kid, onto his third pack of cigarettes, swigged from a Corona.

Ten walked up to him, a swagger in his step. There was an open wound on his cheek, if you could call it that. Maggots had eaten away the mangy flesh, and thick, yellow pus oozed out from the open crater where his cheek used to be. His browned teeth from years of chewing tobacco were cracked and rotten.

"Cancer? Liver failure? A stroke? Which are you hoping for?" Ten asked. Eight looked up at him, flat disinterest clear in his boyish face. Then his gaze landed on the porous remains of Ten's cheek and with a raised eyebrow, looked back to the floor.

"All of them. I want to leave this stinkin' world before I get to Ten."

Ten bristled. "Ten is still young."

Eight shrugged. "Isn't eight years of this enough?" He waved a limp hand toward the sky above.

Ten gazed up at the smoggy sky. It was noon, and the dim light of the sun cast shadows over the land. The acrid smell of smoke and warm, rotting garbage permeated the air, a paradise for swarming gnats. Dry, cracked dirt thirsted for water that had been carefully collected and rationed decades ago. The only meat that remained relatively plentiful was fish, but only for their immunity from the poison that had killed every other living organism around them. The few rats and squirrels that had managed to survive were constantly being hunted for food. The suffocating heat pressed down upon Ten, and he was reminded of the day his mother saved her family from this world and lit their house on fire. Even though he escaped, the villagers cursed him for his family's sin and left him alone in this bitter world.

Twenty-Three hung from high above, her feet swaying limply in the wind. Villagers congregated below the spectacle, whispering the same harsh words they had about Ten's own family.

Dirty cheaters. Taking the easy way out. Leaving before they deserve.

The villagers had discarded Ten outside the village walls, with only a burned cheek as a possible ticket out of this world. Self-harm would always top the list of taboos, even above incest and cannibalism, and blame would always be carried by the one left behind.

Ten had carefully nurtured his wound, caking on anything filthy he could find. With time, the necrosis had spread and he could feel the infection seeping in. He felt lethargic and hot, the burning in his forehead accompanying the heat of the day in the worst way.

"Sepsis?" Eight asked, nodding toward Ten's cheek. Ten nodded.

"It's setting in. I'll be free soon."

Eight gave Ten an admiring glance. "Respectful way to go. Right after cancer."

Ten grinned. "I'd like to give cancer a go. Want to spare me a couple cigarettes?"

Eight looked scandalized. "No way! I went through way too much to get my hands on these! I should be getting more for all the fish I've lugged for the old lady," he grumbled, kicking the smoke hole.

"What if I traded you what I have left of my chewing tobacco?"

Eight stuck out his hand. "Deal."

Ten rummaged through his pockets, looking for the small tin container. "Dang it," he muttered.

Eight shrugged. "Deal's off then."

"Wait!" Ten dropped a wad of thin gold foil, slightly warm, into Eight's hands.

"What is—" Eight's words died upon his lips. The chunk of creamy brown had been reduced to a thick paste from the heat, but Eight lapped it up readily, the sugar unfamiliar but bringing a rush of pleasure. He dropped his last few cigarettes into Ten's hands.

Ten settled down next to Eight, taking a drag from one of his cigarettes. He was silent as Thirty entered the fish shop across the street, tugging along her children. She stopped as her child scooped up a fistful of soot in his grimy hands. She didn't stop him from letting the blackened dust go, little by little, to drift in the hot breeze. Ten was reminded of his own family and their little comforts: boxes of cereal and the occasional trout his father caught. They had seemed content—at least, till the day they damned themselves.

Ten turned to Eight. "Can you imagine what it must be like? To live in a world where people are actually happy? Where grass exists and the day is brighter than the night?"

"And where the air smells clean and full of flowers. Where people look to cure cancer and not die from it. Where accomplishment lies in longevity and not early, drawn-out death. Where names matter and not just for the sake of keeping track of how many dreaded years you've lived?" Eight grunted.

Ten considered this. "I can't even imagine a place like that. When I close my eyes, I want to see color, not flames and people suffering. Not death, or bombs, or rotting flesh. I want to see . . . no, I want to feel what happiness is. Just once."

Forty leaned heavily upon her gnarled walker, just in front of the two boys. She carefully unwrapped a filthy cloth from her stump of a leg. She smiled grimly at the infection beneath.

Forty-One coughed up blood nearby, stumbling as his hacking racked his whole body.

Forty-Three just sat there, only a couple of meters away from Eight and Ten, staring listlessly into the distance.

The three old vagabonds were persistent in their pain. They went through the rounds of yearning for death, same as everyone, but hung on despite their misery.

Eight shook his head, eyes still lingering upon the red staining Forty-One's hands. "Forget your dream." Silence hovered heavy between the two boys. Eight broke it. "How long?" he asked.

"Oh, I don't know. Not long. Who knows? Maybe today, maybe tomorrow. Maybe not for another year."

Fifty stood above his lost son, eyes closed, head bowed, hands roughened with hardship pressed together. But it wasn't grief that settled into the lines of his face, it was relief, relief found on the members of two weathered generations.

Eight bit his lip, chewed at the red, bleeding sores already present. He grabbed Ten's hand and pressed in a folded piece of parchment.

Ten opened the paper cautiously, for fear of tearing at the worn paper that had been opened and folded hundreds of times.

What Ten saw was rather unremarkable. With a child's skill, flowers and meadow had been sketched onto the paper. A multitude of animals crowded the paper, many the size of trees. An unsteady hand had colored in the flowers and the trees, never staying within the lines. But there were colors on this drawing, vivid and unfaded, brighter than any he was used to seeing.

"How . . . did you . . . ?"

"An old man from the fish shop once let me use his crayons and paper long ago. Bragged that his crayons were the few left on Earth. Never saw him again."

Ten gripped the paper in both hands. "Thank you."

"You need it more than me." Eight grunted, pushing against the brick wall to steady himself. He shook his legs and stretched. He trudged away, his dragging feet kicking up a cloud of dust.

Gratitude. The feeling welled deep in Ten's chest and constricted his throat. For the first time, he could see something not so dreary and angry and dry. A calm came over him, loosening tension he had always carried.

The tingling in his fingertips where they brushed soft ash became the sensation of fingering the finest sand, where the sun warmed him and the quiet soothed him. And for a second, Ten thought he felt a cool breeze, carrying the whisper of good things to come. His vision blurred, he forgot about all his misfortune and loneliness, and only saw bright-blue skies and heard the sound of laughter in his dreams.

# Leaving Silence

**DEVONY HOF**, Grade 11, Age 16. Palo Alto High School, Palo Alto, CA.
Rodney Satterthwaite, *Educator*

She was born with no mouth. When her mother bore her on a frigid night in the heart of a bustling city, she uttered no cry. The only sounds were the mother's sobbing and the nurse panicking. Rain drizzled outside and the sky listened for a little sound amid a city full of people, telling old stories as they warmed their hands around the fire. In the sky, the stars listened for the bright cry of a newborn to echo in their old hearts. All they heard was silence. Humans are loud. They fill the world with so much sound. But that spot of silence seemed to diminish the rest.

The mother was exhausted. She did not hold the baby, instead turning one shoulder over to sleep, her sobs hiccuping into the damp pillow. The nurse, who'd been called to the house a few hours before, cleaned the babe and examined her for any mouth. But that spot beneath her button nose was smooth skin. How could she eat with no mouth? How could she speak or sing or scream?

The father took the child and placed it in a cradle he'd made in preparation. Angels were carved in it, with mouths open in song. But the father felt as though he were placing a child of the devil into a cradle he'd made with such joy in his heart.

When the parents awoke in the morning, the child was hot with a fever. Her chest rose and fell with short breaths. Desperately, the mother tried to soothe her. She blamed herself for her moment of weakness, letting the child sleep away from her mother's arms. The father only watched as his wife tried frantically to cure the child's ailment. Perhaps, he said, it would be better to let her die now rather than remain a burden on the family. The wife steadfastly refused. But as the baby's pulse weakened, her hopes did as well.

The mother paced around the room holding her daughter, till she passed by the small window in their home. Fresh air filtered through the window, and suddenly the child's breathing eased, her cheeks changed from sickly pale to a gentle rosy pink. The mother watched in wonder as the golden rays sparked her baby's wide blue eyes. She fed on sunshine and fresh air. The father stood to the side and felt his soul darken. This was a curse like no other. The child would have to go outside at least a few times a day. Her deformity would have to be seen by the townsfolk.

As the child grew, her hair came black and wild. Her darkblue eyes stayed their strange color. While she could not speak, she would nod or shake her head, and respond when called.

Her mother called her Aoide, named for the muse of voice and song, and she hardly ever left her side. As Aoide had to go outside every few hours, her deformity would have to be hidden. So Aoide's mother gave her a scarf to wrap around her lower face. Aoide's inability to speak wouldn't go unnoticed, but at least the neighborhood wouldn't have to see the reason. Once Aoide got her daily fill of fresh air, her mother whisked her back into the small stuffy house and set her down in a chair near the fire while she went about her daily chores.

In these moments, Aoide longed to rip off her scarf and coat and run out the door, let her hair run in the wind behind her. She'd run to those green hills she'd seen in the distance, muddled by the haze of the city. She would listen to the quiet sounds of nature, the ones that no one else but she could hear. Her silent voice had sharpened her ear. The air would fill her up and Aoide would never go hungry again.

If she could write, perhaps Aoide would have told her mother this. But her mother was illiterate, coming from a poor un-educated family. Aoide's father could read, but he'd never even taught his daughter the alphabet. The only words she saw were those scratched in the dirt roads by the little children across the way, who were going to a school downtown.

One day, when Aoide was eight, she saw two children using sticks to write in the dirt, very intent on their activity. Sud-denly curious, she carefully slipped across the road.

She tapped the boy on the shoulder and pointed at the ground. He nodded and smiled.

"I'm writing my name!" he exclaimed, "It's very long."

Aoide nodded.

"What's your name?"

She shook her head sadly. Now the little girl was looking at her as well. "What do you want?" she asked.

Aoide pointed at their sticks and at the ground. They real-ized her requested and handed one to her. She bent down in the dirt with them and pointed at the first letter the little boy had written.

"That's a C," he explained. "My name's Christopher."

Aoide nodded and carefully copied the curve. Her eyes brightened, and she leaned over the boy's work to look at the next symbol. In her fascination, she didn't notice when her scarf slipped off. The little boy and girl only had to look at her face for one second before screaming. Aoide immediately leapt up and stumbled away from the pair, covering her face with her hands. The little boy began to sob.

Frantically, Aoide ran back across the street, the screams echoing in her ears. Then she rushed into her house, slamming the door closed.

Her ears ringing, Aoide glanced around the room, her eyes landing on a knife, gleaming on the stovetop. She grabbed it and stood before a mirror. Very deliberately she began to cut a jagged line across the bottom of her face, a couple centimeters below the nose. Aoide tried to make the ends curl up like a smile, but blood coursed across her hand and made her fingers slippery. She dropped the knife on the floor and stared at the bloody mess her face had become. She tried to scream, but the mouth she'd created wouldn't work, it would only bleed.

Her mother came in, asking about the ruckus she'd heard on the streets. She screamed in horror, not at the absence of a mouth, but at the horrifying mouth her daughter had created. The nurse who'd brought her into the world years before was called, and she stitched up the wound. It healed well, though it was very painful, but there was always a faint line, a permanent scar.

Aoide was sixteen. Her mother trusted her enough now to be able to take care of her own needs and not venture out too far into the city. But there was rarely time for Aoide to really slip away. Her mother was always around the house, and she noticed if Aoide was gone for too long. Now though, her mother had a job farther downtown. She'd be gone for hours a day.

So once her mother left to go to work that morning, Aoide slipped the scarf around her face and set out to explore. At first, all was as she regularly observed, with men and women rushing about their business, and poor people slinking around the edges of the streets, miserable and hungry.

But then, a gorgeous sound filled Aoide's keen ears. A sound that was beautiful and merry and heartwarming all at once. She turned a corner and glimpsed the source of this sound. A street musician, playing his violin. His muddy hat was on the ground, a few copper coins in it, and his hair was getting blown about by the wind. Aoide approached, her eyes filled to the brim with wonder, and listened. Soon the musician switched to another song, one much more melancholy and tragic. Aoide began to follow his quick fingers, and her understanding grew as she stayed standing there for what seemed like hours, entranced by his playing.

At last he stopped and looked up at her. "You ain't got no money do yeh?" he muttered.

Shocked out of her musical reverie, Aoide could only shake her head. He stared at her, puzzled, and then leaned down to pocket the change and place the hat back on his head.

"Well this is the last time for me anyhow," he said, sighing. "I'm gonna be workin' in a factory now. Pays better than this."

Aoide nodded, her eyes still on the instrument. The musician frowned.

"Now you listen. You 'aven't said a thing, but I think you like this ol' violin and I 'ave no use for it anymore, so you better 'ave it. I wanted to get a few coins fer it, but no one's goin' to take this piece o' junk."

Then, reluctantly, he clicked the violin and bow into his case and handed it to Aoide. Her eyes wide in surprise, she accepted the gift. Instinctively, her hand went to her scarf, but she was safe. And now she had this instrument, something of great and mysterious beauty.

Hearing no thanks, the tired musician tipped his hat and

started off. But before he'd turned away completely, Aoide grabbed her skirts to slip into a curtsey. The man laughed and began to whistle a tune as he walked down the grubby streets.

Aoide managed to keep her violin a secret. She stowed it away under her bed, and when her parents had left the house she practiced.

The moment her fingers felt the strings, she felt a part of her open up, like a newborn taking its first breath. The notes didn't seem to come from the violin but from somewhere deep inside herself. And soon, despite having never seen a sheet of music, Aoide was composing her own works. Her fingers were delicate and quick, and they became her mouthpiece. Once she felt brave enough, she ventured onto the streets. She did not lay down a hat for coins.

People came to listen. Aoide would have had fear of the scrutiny, but her music formed a cloak that hid her, yet revealed something of her. People let coins fall onto the dirt in a little pile next to her feet, but she left them there for the people who roamed at night to pick up.

Her parents smelled the odors of the street that clung to her clothing, but strangely enough they never said a thing. The joy that lifted Aoide's every step was like a tiny candle, small and unnoticeable, easy to blow out if need be. They ignored it much of the time and continued to stumble in the dark.

One winter day, as Aoide's breath formed ethereal clouds around her instrument, someone in the audience spoke to her. Usually the people who stopped and listened to her songs were silent, caught up in the enchanting melodies. But this visitor nearly tripped over himself in shock.

"Aoide? Is that you?"

Aoide lifted her eyes to see her father standing there, his work satchel slipping off his shoulder. His eyes were white with shock, and he stared at the instrument his daughter held in her long delicate fingers. Behind him Aoide's mother peered out. They must have gone for lunch in town.

A short silence followed as Aoide slowly let her bow slide off the strings. She frowned slightly, and then in one sweeping motion, she took off the scarf. Then she placed the bow back on the strings and started to play again. The people who'd been watching her performance parted as she walked through them, still playing. Her mother reached out her arm and her lips parted. Then she pulled back and gave an almost imperceptible nod toward her daughter, her eyes glossing over with tears. Aoide's father stepped back with the crowd and turned away, so only her mother watched as her daughter faded into the distance, walking toward the patch of green on the horizon.

# The Permanence of Plastic

**MEGHNA PAMULA**, Grade 9, Age 14. Dougherty Valley High School, San Ramon, CA. Caroline Lloyd, *Educator*

It is unlikely that anybody would like to live in a world in which there are no birds chirping and no fish swimming. While oceans make up 71% of Earth's surface, they are in critical condition (Oceanic Institute). Plagued by an unconcealed yet ignored monster—trash—our oceans are declining in purity. With 8 million tons being dumped into oceans every year, plastic pollution is no doubt an enemy to marine life (National Geographic). Already there are enormous islands of garbage in the middle of our oceans, and we are not far from a total trash takeover destroying all ocean life.

Though garbage exists in some form in nearly every stretch of sea, there are five major locations on Earth where trash gathers and gets trapped in a cycle that prevents it from moving elsewhere. These locations, called ocean gyres, are also described as "trash vortexes," because they trap marine debris and never allow it to flow out to shore. Trash is sucked into these currents. Any litter on beaches or trash flushed down toilets is very likely to end up in a trash vortex because these vortexes suck in all debris, especially miniscule materials.

These large, dense "black holes" of trash are extremely harmful to every species of marine life.

Much of the garbage in these trash vortexes is plastic litter. This example of human disregard for the environment causes a ripple effect, in which the plastic floats out into the ocean and stays there forever. Because plastic is not biodegradable, it simply breaks into smaller pieces as its exposure to sunlight increases, meaning it will never truly disappear from the ocean. Plastic fragments can become as small as sesame seeds, at which point they become microplastics. Microplastics are not just the result of littered plastic; they can also get into the ocean in other ways, such as being washed out of synthetic clothing. Marcus Eriksen, a co-founder of the 5 Gyres Institute, an organization dedicated to reducing plastic pollution, describes marine microplastics as a "plastic smog throughout the world's oceans" (Marine Plastic Bulletin).

Another enemy to marine life is the microbead. Beauty companies contribute sizable amounts of microplastics to the ocean through exfoliating scrubs. The miniscule beads in these scrubs are made of plastic, and when washed down the drain, they have the same effect on ocean life that disintegrating microplastics have. Many animals mistake microbeads for fish eggs and choke when they try to swallow them. Like microbeads, other plastic items bear close resemblance to prey for many ocean creatures. For example, after balloons get torn apart, they look very similar to jellyfish. Similarly, plastic bags can resemble kelp. Both balloons and plastic bags often strangle animals or cause them to choke. Another reason many animals eat plastic is because it smells like food. This most commonly affects seabirds, which eat krill. Krill consume algae, which, as they decompose, emit a sulfuric odor known as dimethyl sulfide (National Geographic). This smell allows seabirds to find krill. A lot of algae collect on floating plastic, so when seabirds catch a whiff of the sulfuric odor, they feed on that plastic, thinking it is krill. For this reason, more than 90% of seabirds have plastic fragments in their stomachs (Plastic Oceans).

Numerous species are affected by plastic pollution in the ocean, and the associated statistics are alarming. In fact, about 100,000 marine animals and 1 million seabirds are found dead from plastic or plastic entanglement each year (Ocean Crusaders). Additionally, 200 areas on Earth, called dead zones, are so polluted that life can no longer exist there. Not all of these areas are underwater, however. Dead zones exist on land as well, and pristine environments are slowly becoming polluted too.

During my recent visit to Yellowstone National Park, one of the most pure and untouched places in the world, I witnessed a coyote at a distance attempting to eat a plastic water bottle. It seemed as though the coyote was trying to get to the water that remained in the bottle, but once it managed to get the lid off and all the water spilled out, it kept chewing on the bottle, perhaps thinking it was something edible. This went on for about twenty minutes as the onlookers gazed at the scene with concern, wondering what the animal would do. From the relentless pursuit of the animal, it was clear that it could have choked to death had it not finally dropped the bottle in fear when a woman gingerly walked her way toward the animal to scare it away for its own safety.

Increased plastic in oceans results in decreased ecosystem stability. According to the World Economic Forum and the Ellen MacArthur Foundation, by the year 2050, there will be more plastic in the world's oceans than fish. This will be a turning point, because it is likely that the rate of environmental destruction will accelerate greatly after that. There will be a decline in biodiversity, so animals that help humans progress in various ways will start to die out. For example, sea lions, seals, and narwhals all help scientists track climate change. Plastic in the ocean is a considerable threat to these species, so their numbers would dwindle greatly. With the loss of these creatures and others, it would become extremely difficult to track climate change, making it more prevalent in every region of the world. Atmospheric carbon dioxide levels would increase, which would harm the Earth in numerous ways, such as by causing longer droughts and more wildfires.

As more plastic is dumped into the ocean, our lives on land will become more polluted as well. Plastic litter floating in ocean water absorbs toxic pollutants, such as polychlorinated biphenyl and polycyclic aromatic hydrocarbon, both of which have been proven to cause cancer. Plastic in oceans also alters the food chain, and the impacts of this can be drastic. The food chain is arranged in "ripples," meaning those that are immediately affected do not suffer as much as the later affected species, which are humans in this case. For example, if one species of amphibians goes extinct because of excess plastic pollution in their habitat, their predators, largemouth bass, will be affected. Humans, who feed on the bass, will be impacted even more negatively. This is just one possible food chain. Many food chains come together to make a food web, and the harmful effects to humans are vastly amplified at this point.

The best way to combat ocean pollution is to prevent plastic from entering oceans, sewage systems, rivers, lakes, etc. This involves people making minor changes, such as recycling or terminating their use of single-use plastics. Avoiding products with microbeads is effective, as microbead concentration in oceans is increasing rapidly. This can be done by exfoliating with a towel if necessary or by using natural exfoliants, such as baking soda or oatmeal. Not purchasing bottled water is another fantastic way to decrease a person's own plastic consumption and eventually contribute less to overall emissions. Anything that is wrapped individually contributes to overall plastic pollution. Buying in bulk means far less plastic that could end up in the water, and this option is cheaper too. Finally, supporting plastic bans and organizations addressing plastic pollution can help greatly.

In my hometown, one very effective change has been made to try to lower our town's plastic output. Grocery stores now charge customers at the checkout line for plastic bags that they request to carry their items. This has had a great impact, as many people now bring their own reusable bags, such as tote bags, when shopping. Community effort is an essential part of ending plastic pollution in our oceans.

With Earth's current population at 7.6 billion and a projected population of 9.8 billion by 2050, the amount of plastic pollution in the oceans will increase exponentially if we do not recognize and fight this issue (United Nations, Department of Economic and Social Affairs). Let us take action to make a significant difference that can preserve our planet's splendor and beauty. Let us join together to make efforts to stop dumping plastic into our oceans. As David Attenborough, naturalist and broadcaster says, "There is no away—because plastic is so permanent and so indestructible. When you cast it into the ocean, it doesn't go away" (Plastic Oceans). We are at a point where the oceans are in a critical condition; they can be saved or lost forever. The carelessness of our ways will come back to haunt us when our ocean life is lost but our garbage remains.

# What "Finsta" Culture Says About Modern Teenagers

**JULIA SPANDE**, Grade 12, Age 16. Harborfields High School, Greenlawn, NY. Jim Incorvaia, *Educator*

I was admiring a portrait of my friend's dog on Instagram when I noticed a comment from a strange username. It was an All Star lyric (yes, that band that you only ever associate with Shrek) with a girl's name slapped in the center. At first, I dismissed it as a strange spam account, but then I saw my friend had replied to the comment. After clicking on the profile, I realized it was the girl who sat behind me in math class pictured in neon shutter shades. Wait, wasn't I already following this girl? I searched her name and a different account popped up immediately, her first and last name as the username and a beaming selfie as the profile picture. I had encountered my first finsta.

The username will be close to the name of someone you know, but with some cringe-worthy, 2007 MySpace-username flair thrown in for kicks. The profile picture is most likely a bad selfie—a picture from a time when duck face was unironically popular, or perhaps a dog filter Snapchat. The bio resembles something a twelve-year-old would write, except with even more emojis. The entire account oozes irony, dares to be taken seriously.

Finstas, or "fake" Instagram accounts, are designed to be taken lightly. Unlike a "real" Instagram account (rinsta), you can post virtually anything you want on your finsta without social repercussions. Pictures don't have to be filtered or aesthetically pleasing. They don't have to look appealing or depict anything you're proud of. It's okay to post unattractive pictures, encouraged even. Finsta houses blurry pictures of mac and cheese and homegrown carpool karaoke videos. Captions aren't as succinct or witty as they are on rinsta accounts. You can rant about *The Bachelor* or an exam you're dreading. Finsta is a social media free-for-all, and it's gaining traction.

"My finsta is my favorite social media account," reports one nineteen-year-old college freshman. "It's like my own personal space. I choose who follows me and what I want to say and show people. I can show my real personality."

This sentiment is echoed by others. "I have a finsta because, well, I wanted to show a different side of me than my main account," says one high school senior. "I can tailor it to me and my friends."

In many ways, finsta is like a more efficient group chat: You can communicate your thoughts to all your friends without hassle. Finsta users trust that what they say will remain among their followers and themselves. And because the incentive of a second Instagram account is free self-expression and not popularity, most users keep their accounts small—under one hundred followers. It is not taboo to deny the follow requests of classmates you don't talk to or don't like. You wouldn't text that girl who sits three rows behind you in your psych lecture all about your horrible breakup, so she doesn't follow your finsta. It's a simple system.

As I learned more about Finsta-gram from my friends, I was reassured that these secondary Instagram accounts are worthwhile. A personally curated internet biome sounds idyllic. Who doesn't want a place to be themselves and be heard at the same time?

The mass appeal of Finsta-gram highlights "real" Instagram's faults: It's about business showmanship, not self-expression. Teenagers watch as peers like James Charles, Loren Gray, Danielle Bregoli, and Alexis Ren rise to stardom solely based on their social media presence. While some Instagram stars have talents like singing or dancing, more have mastered the art of branding. They lie on the beach in trendy swimsuits, boast beautiful contours, and make polarizing comments in the name of humor. And they make money—a lot of it—by marketing products to their teenage followers.

These teenage "icons" are fundamentally no different from the average person in my biology class. Every teenager I've talked to acknowledges that. It's not the figures themselves who entrance young people: it's the consumerist lifestyles they lead. Rinsta culture eschews realness in favor of aesthetics, and teens are pressured into following the latest trends and leading glamorous lives. Editing pictures makes casual snaps look more professional; you pay for software or photo filters on VSCO Cam. You look more popular surrounded by friends and red Solo cups; you go to that party hosted by someone you hate and take pictures. This brand of swimsuit is slimming, this brand of highlighter makes your face glow, this brand of sweatshirt makes you look like a Soundcloud rapper: You buy them all. You make the coolest version of yourself available to your peers in the hopes of staving off insecurity. Instagram is now a branding platform for people with nothing to sell.

Take, for example, Sofia, a recently graduated high school senior. Through both Instagram and the now-deceased Vine, she's amassed over 30,000 followers, more people than live in her town. "Yeah, it's really weird to have such a huge following," she says. "It's cool because my followers are really sweet, and I'm well known around school now. But I get a lot of DMs [direct messages] from companies asking me what my brand is and if I want to do spon [sponsored] stuff. Like, I'm a high school girl going to be a college student. I don't have a brand."

The finsta trend is a warning sign, but not in the alarmist "we need to stop these kids posting nudes, bullying each other, and shooting up heroin" way many child psychologists would have you believe. Teenagers feel hemmed in by the constant social marketing expected of them. They need spaces to be who they are—messy, weird, goofy, unappealing, rough-around-the-edges human beings. They want to free themselves from the current social media rules, where every post has to fit a brand, every possible follower needs to be harvested, and every possible occasion to look cool has to be documented. Coming from a teenager, Instagram isn't fun anymore. The app we once used to post goofy pictures of friends and chat about TV shows has turned into a source of pressure. Finsta is a way to take back the social media we once knew—the aesthetically unappealing, boundless, happiness-driven accounts. Accounts from a time before teenagers became the target of every corporation's new ad campaign.

And for all the concerned columnists describing finsta as a pathway toward illegal activity? You'll find a thousand unposed mirror selfies before you come across anything of interest.

# Lannister Policies in Counterinsurgency

**JACKSON EHRENWORTH**, Grade 12, Age 18. Avenues: The World School, New York, NY. Ron Widelac, *Educator*

In the early hours of a spring morning, a young woman crawled over crumbled rubble through a haze of smoke toward a door. She was barefoot and burning. Flames crept up her body, scorching the skin from her legs, back, and neck. A carefully picked T-shirt with a logo for her favorite band melted swiftly onto her torso. Though she was no more than twenty-eight, she would not live through this morning, and she would never know who sent the missiles that left her to burn alive in her small office, unable to open a melted door. It was not quick. Co-workers heard her cries, and then her screams, as the one hand she had left melted to the face she was trying to protect.

On the other side of the door was a community of pain. Her friend hung from the building upside down. In an hour, both his legs would be amputated. It was an easier death than hers. Sixteen co-workers would die that day, thirty-eight would be maimed and scarred. When rescue squads arrived to wade through the fifteen feet of rubble that had been a four-story building, first they had to wait for the mile-high dust cloud to subside.

Death by terror is not the result of accident or a spasm of calamity, the ravages of misadventure or a natural disaster. It is the deliberate taking of human life with extreme violence. It occurs because someone, somewhere, decided that people should die. For decades, the world has developed technology to kill people more precisely. Satellites can pinpoint buildings; drones can deliver death remotely.

The Geneva Convention defines war crimes as acts that "endanger protected persons or objects or breach important values" (ICRC, 2015). Protected persons includes civilian populations or civilian individuals.

The young woman was a civilian make-up artist. Her coworkers were technicians and journalists. The bomb site was Serb TV. The missiles were sent by NATO. It was not an accident. It was not collateral damage on the periphery of a military target. The girl, the workers, the journalists—they were the target. In the decade and a half since 9/11, the U.S. and its allies have committed to counterterrorism methodologies that include invasion, bombing of civilian targets, and assaults on civilians. Along the way, people have come to believe that civilian deaths are not only acceptable but suitable. More than that, there really isn't any notion of civilian at all. The very notion of a "civilian citizen" has come to be a signifier of "us," while anyone who is perceived to be related in religion, ethnicity, or location to a perceived enemy has come to be a signifier for "target."

The truth is that acts of terror will occur, and people will die alone and in fear, and that nations must make efforts to counter these attacks. Counterinsurgency, though, must hold itself to the ideals that it is purporting to protect. Over the past decade, in the process of waging a war on terror, the U.S. and its allies have adopted both the strategies and mentality of those whom they condemn. What the U.S. calls war crimes on the part of others is in danger of becoming its own counterinsurgency methodology. This antihumanitarian methodology is manifested most distinctly through: the profiling of journalists as military targets; the conceptualizing of civilian centers such as hospitals as propaganda centers and thus also military targets; and the normalization of collateral damage to civilians as inevitable to successful counterinsurgency.

The decision to make the killing of journalists a valid military objective can be seen early in the timeline of Western antiterror policy. The clearest example of this policy is the bombing of Serb TV by NATO. It was April 23, 1999. Serbia and Kosovo were engaged in a vicious struggle over independence. NATO, citing Serbian human rights abuses, sided with Kosovo. NATO launched an extended missile attack. One of NATO's earliest targets: the Serb TV station. It was manned mostly by young volunteer journalists and technicians.

*New York Times* journalist Steven Erlanger described the scene of the NATO bombing thus: "Everything crashed. There was no way out. There was smoke everywhere. It was terrible. People were screaming. It was like a nightmare." There was a "huge detonation, and everything went completely dark." Erlanger chose his words deliberately. He used a narrative technique used by fiction writers. He invoked the sympathy of the reader by giving access to the experiences and inner thinking of the characters. It was, he wrote, "an increasingly familiar one of smashed glass, broken walls, twisted timbers, scorched paint and emotional devastation" (Erlanger, 1999).

Images of NATO airstrikes make a paradoxical contrast with the purported aim to end human rights abuses and the death of civilians. Here is where the thinking becomes as important as the act. The decision to bomb Serb TV was justified by Western leaders agreeing that journalists were legitimate targets. Noam Chomsky, analyzing the rhetoric of the attack, cites: "Richard Holbrooke, then envoy to Yugoslavia, described the successful attack on RTV as 'an enormously important, and, I think, positive development,' a sentiment echoed by others" (Chomsky, 2015). British leader Tony Blair also called the decision "entirely justified," and Kenneth Bacon, a Pentagon spokesman, defended the massacre, saying that "Serb TV is as much a part of Milosevic's murder machine as his military is" (Erlanger, 1999).

As Chomsky points out, there is an irony here, considering the cries of outrage and "We are Charlie Hebdo!" that erupted when Western journalists were targeted for death. There is a bitter disparity of reactions between the outrage at the murder of Charlie Hebdo and French journalists, and the righteousness, even gleefulness of Western leaders claiming that enemy journalists are viable military targets. Thinking about this disparity, Chomsky suggests that war crimes committed against us are considered terrorism, and those we commit are considered part of a legitimate war effort. It is hard not to see a moral emptiness to the discourse of NATO and Western allies. It is disturbing in two ways. Either leaders know that it is morally wrong to target journalists and it illustrates a deliberate propaganda campaign aimed at positioning any desired target as justifiable in order to rally public opinion, or it demonstrates an inability to perceive anyone other than us as fully human.

In the counterinsurgency timeline, the move from targeting journalists to targeting doctors might not seem such a big one. It marks a subtle and important stance, however: the conceptualizing of civilian centers such as hospitals as potential propaganda sites and thus legitimate military targets. The deliberate assault on a hospital in Fallujah by U.S. forces in November 2004 is a notable example of this policy. Chomsky says of this war and of this incident: "It's interesting to look at it carefully. Fallujah, first of all, was one of the worst atrocities of the 21st century. The Iraq war itself was the worst crime of the 21st century, easily. Fallujah was probably the worst war crime carried out during that war" (quoted in Larkin, 2015).

Chomsky goes on to describe the event: "Seven thousand Marines attacked Fallujah, probably killed everyone who was there. They called them insurgents—whatever that means. On the first day of the invasion of Fallujah, *The New York Times* had a front page photograph of Marines breaking into the general hospital, which is a war crime, and throwing all the patients and doctors on the floor and shackling them. It was hailed as a triumph" (2015). That *Times* article was written by war reporter Richard Oppel. Oppel wrote, on November 8, 2004, the day after the attack, that "Iraqi troops eagerly kicked the doors in, some not waiting for the locks to break. Patients and hospital employees were rushed out of rooms by armed soldiers and ordered to sit or lie on the floor while troops tied their hands behind their backs."

Chomsky's choice of language, the use of the word "shackled," where Oppel uses "tied," illuminates Chomsky's outrage. His outrage reflects overall outrage at the war itself and at the choice of a hospital as a primary assault. What matters most about the assault on the hospital is not what happened there. It is the discourse around the attack. When asked about why they assaulted the hospital, U.S. high command claimed that the hospital "was releasing casualty figures," and therefore it was a propaganda center and legitimate war target (Chomsky, 2015; Oppel, 2004).

Here's the problem with this discourse. It makes two assumptions. The first is that it widens the concept of what counts as propaganda, so that releasing news of civilian casualties caused by U.S. troops qualifies as propaganda. The second is that it assumes that civilian authors of propaganda are legitimate military targets. Both of these assumptions teeter on the brink of humanitarian abuses and war crimes. Journalists and doctors are not legitimate military targets of civilized nations.

Not just the assault on Fallujah hospital, but the numerous civilian casualties of the Iraq war marked a move toward Western acceptance of collateral damage to civilians. CNN reporter Fareed Zakaria called the Iraq war "a failure and a terrible mistake . . . a humanitarian tragedy" (2015). What the war did was condition us to accept civilian casualties.

The normalization of collateral damage to civilians as a natural part of successful counterinsurgency is the most recent and most insidious shift in counterinsurgency. The airstrikes in Syria manifest this willingness on the part of the U.S. to countenance the massacre of civilians. For example, on December 28, 2015, "a U.S.-led coalition airstrike killed at least 50 Syrian civilians when it targeted a headquarters of Islamic State extremists in northern Syria, according to an eyewitness and a Syrian opposition human rights organization" (McClatchy, 2015). McClatchy notes the delay and reluctance of U.S. forces to acknowledge these deaths. Only after repeated inquiries were they affirmed.

According to McClatchy DC, "the Syrian Network for Human Rights, an independent opposition group that tracks casualties in Syria, has documented the deaths of at least 40 civilians in airstrikes in the months between the start of U.S. bombing in Syria on September 23 through the December 28 strike on Al

Bab. The deaths include 13 people killed in Idlib province on the first day of the strikes. Other deaths include 23 civilians killed in the eastern province of Deir el Zour, two in Raqqa province and two more in Idlib province" (2015).

The effect of this kind of indiscriminate bombing is further illustrated by the deaths of doctors with the alliance Doctors Without Borders, when Al Quds Hospital in Aleppo, Syria, was destroyed by a government airstrike on April 27, 2016. At least 27 people were killed. Among them were 3 children and 6 staff members. "This devastating attack has destroyed a vital hospital in Aleppo, and the main referral center for pediatric care in the area," the head of the charity's Syria mission, Muskilda Zancada, said in a statement. "Where is the outrage among those with the power and obligation to stop this carnage?" (Barnard, 2016). This incident was not the first killing of doctors in Syria. In response to prior targeting of doctors, Doctors Without Borders issued a global statement asking for a global "obligation to ensure the protection of humanitarian workers." The agency especially expressed concerns that "such attacks directly impact the ability of aid organizations to provide medical assistance" (MSF, 2013).

The lack of moral outrage that charity and humanitarian workers lament marks the mentality as well as methods of an unethical counterinsurgency policy. The problem with the stance that collateral damage to civilians is acceptable is that when you say it's okay to kill civilians as long as insurgents get killed as well, there is no protection for women and children or ordinary citizens. First journalists, then doctors, then . . . everyone. The lives of those who are not us simply come to be meaningless.

In her allegory *Terrible Things*, Eve Bunting tells the story of animals in a woodland. Every day, someone comes to take away some of the animals, to their death. Each time, the other animals face a moral choice: to protect the innocent or to ignore the violence around them. They choose ignorance. They willfully refuse to see what happens around them. They refuse empathy. In the end, there is no one there to protect the final few. Each decision we make, as individuals, as a government, as a nation, reflects ethical choices. We have to have a moral code we are defending, or the country we are defending is no longer worth defending.

There is also the question of whether ruthless and antihumanitarian tactics work. In his fight for civil rights, Dr. Martin Luther King Jr. stated that "darkness cannot drive out darkness; only light can do that" (1957). In his analysis of the Iraq war, analyst Loren Thompson notes that each civilian killed, each child's death, each hospital bombed or burned, stirred up opposition. "If anything," Thompson notes, "our presence helped spur recruiting by sectarian militias and local supporters of Al Qaeda" (2011). The reason that insurgency recruiting increased is that U.S. actions were seen as not only threatening but inhumane.

The notion that other people's lives don't matter will not, in the end, garner the support of greater civilized communities. It's a Lannister-type *Game of Thrones* policy, exemplified when Jamie Lannister exclaims, "F*** anyone who isn't us." The thing is, though, that the Lannisters lose all their support, not because they weren't strong, but because they weren't good.

The U.S. has slipped into counterinsurgency methods that mirror the war crimes and atrocities of those we claim to be better than and are fighting against. We need to amend these policies, for they fuel the justifiable scorn of those we attack, and create a legacy of hypocrisy and hatred from which we, like Bunting's woodland animals, may not emerge.

**JACQUELYN HELLYER**, *Waking Up*, Drawing & Illustration. Grade 12, Age 17, Oswego High School, Oswego, IL. Michael Skura, *Educator*

# This Is Us, It Always Has Been

**RYAN KIM**, Grade 11, Age 16. Roslyn High School, Roslyn Heights, NY.
Marigrace Cirringione, *Educator*

On the morning of August 12, 2017, a large crowd of white nationalists and other right-wing groups assembled at Emancipation Park in Charlottesville, Virginia. Many were carrying signs, and some, improvised handmade weapons. The aim of the rally was to oppose the removal of a statue of Robert E. Lee, a Confederate general, from the park. Waiting for them was an equally defiant group of counterprotesters, there to vehemently push back against the racist rhetoric of the former. The surrounding area quickly became a disastrous cluster of punches, swinging bats, and pepper spray. Police officers in riot gear worked futilely to mitigate the violence. Then, in the early afternoon, the violence escalated to the point that one individual rammed his car into a crowd, killing one counterprotester. In all, three people died and more than thirty people were injured because of the chaotic events of the rally.

Government leaders, the media, and social pundits were quick to condemn the events at Charlottesville. The general sentiment, even across party lines, was that this was a time for unity, not partisan rhetoric. After all—conservative or liberal, Democrat or Republican—what happened was not representative of the United States of America. Larry Hogan, the Republican governor of Maryland, stated that acts like what transpired in Charlottesville had no place in society and that "American values [had] nothing to do with white supremacy and hate." Mark Warner, the Democratic senator from Virginia, echoed this sentiment, demanding that white nationalists "go back to where [they] came from." Over and again, the nation adopted the mantra "this is not us." What happened was deemed a rogue, abhorrent act by a far-right minority, a growing but insular group that stood for values that America did not condone.

But the "this is not us" narrative is a fiction. To say that white supremacy, xenophobia, bigotry, and violence are foreign to America is plain untrue. At best, this view stems from shortsightedness and a superficial understanding of our history. At its worst, it is a blatant attempt to revise, sanitize and falsify our past. Whether accidental or deliberate, the idea that events like Charlottesville are foreign to our American identity perpetuates a longstanding tradition of American Exceptionalism.

While the idea of American Exceptionalism has no formal definition, its first use within the American vernacular can be traced to the Puritan settlers. Upon landing in New England, John Winthrop, future governor of the Massachusetts Bay Colony, urged his fellow settlers to be a "city upon a hill," a model example for the world (Beeley). Years later, the designers of the Statue of Liberty made sure to utilize Emma Lazarus's poem, which reads in part "Give me your tired, your poor . . ." as if America's welcoming arms were a messianic reprieve to incoming immigrants from the hardships abroad. Even in today's political climate, it is generally believed that America is an "indispensible nation" (Clinton) and the greatest country in the world (Jones). American Exceptionalism is an ideology that doesn't just invoke the term "special" when one thinks of America, but rather invokes something deeper: a belief that America follows a historically different route in terms of governance and morals.

To be sure, there is nothing inherently wrong with the belief that one's country should serve as a model example for other nations. But American Exceptionalism uses the idea as a pretense to gloss over unsavory events and/or people in our nation. When we see images of white nationalists marching defiantly in support of Confederate heroes or read about high school and college students uploading videos with racist rants to social media, we cannot merely brush these individuals off as the "other." To say they do not represent us is to forget our complicated past and dishonor its victims. We are a country that was built on the backs of slaves, a country responsible for Jim Crow, lynchings, and Japanese internment. We are a nation guilty of racially profiling Muslims and forced assimilation of Native Americans. Charlottesville is no different, it is also a part of who we are.

To say otherwise and deny it is not only disingenuous, but it stunts our ability to address the root of the problem. We cannot point fingers at a few wrongdoers without acknowledging our own complicity. Otherwise our denial of racism and our racist past is its own form of racism, a more dangerous kind since it is cloaked in a false sense of rightness. We need to abandon this rhetoric of constantly working to disassociate ourselves from the white supremacists, the radical nationalists, the racists. We must abandon our psychological naiveté and accept that these "bad things" have been and always will be part of America's history.

# The Worst Kind of Goodbye

**MAYA ROBLES**, Grade 11, Age 17. John Cooper School, The Woodlands, TX. Peter Elliott, *Educator*

(Note: Every time the word *goodbye* is read by a female, she moves her lips to mouth the word; however, no sound should be made. Instead, the male on stage should say the word.)

[Enter MALE from stage right to sit on a chair facing the audience at downstage center stage, almost uncomfortably close to the audience. FEMALE 1 should be centered, but on a platform further upstage. FEMALE 4 is downstage left. FEMALE 2 is center right and FEMALE 3 is far stage right.]

FEMALE 1: The worst kind of—

MALE: Goodbye

FEMALE 2: —is when you don't even consider it an option, because six months ago he was telling you that you were the only one, and now the word *forever* isn't even uttered from his lips. Four months ago, he was looking at you like you put the sun in the sky, and now he looks at you like he can't wait for it to set and leave the horizons over his head.

The worst kind of—

MALE: Goodbye

FEMALE 4: —is going everywhere and seeing the parts of him you never saw before. Like his favorite color painted in the morning's sky or the smell of his neck in the aisles of a pharmacy. You wish more than anything not to remember, but how could one forget? Your hardest nights are the ones spent drunk on an aging feeling.

The worst kind of—

MALE: Goodbye

FEMALE 1: —is the kind that you dread. You feel it leaking into every crevice of your skin, and you'll try not to talk because you can hardly take a breath in, let alone beg him to stay while you picture him stabbing wounds like "Let's end this" and "I can't do this anymore." You're holding in your tears when you're alone at night and replacing them with anger and words with a lot more bark than bite, like "fine, okay, leave, Jesus Christ, I don't even want you anymore." And you imagine he'll look at you all sad because he knows that you're lying, but God, fuck if he's going to leave then just rip off the Band-Aid and don't wait around to see if the wound will heal.

(pause)

The worst kind of—

MALE: Goodbye

FEMALE 3: —is the kind that echoes through your body months later because his presence left fingerprints on parts of your body that you couldn't expect, like the back of your eyelids or the spaces between your fingertips.

The worst kind of—

MALE: Goodbye

FEMALE 4: —is the kind that enters like a bullet but slowly and painfully crawls its way out like the blood from a cut. You feel it everywhere and you let it haunt you because you'd rather picture him saying—

MALE: Goodbye

FEMALE 4: .0The worst kind of—

MALE: Goodbye

FEMALE 2: —is the kind you can sleep off. You can lie in bed each night and fabricate a new excuse as to why he walked out that door, crafting it with desperate hands and shaky movements, but you know even fever dreams have a tendency to be forgotten over time.
    The worst kind of—

MALE: Goodbye

FEMALE 1: —is the kind that he left you, because no matter what you do, you can't seem to press the right buttons to rewind, or close your eyes hard enough to shove the words back into his mouth and replace it with the happiness you could've sworn he once felt.
(Lights fade.)

# Kings of Men

**MOLLIE PATE**, Grade 12, Age 17. Charleston County School of the Arts, North Charleston, SC. Danielle DeTiberus, Francis Hammes, and Elizabeth Hart, *Educators*

[A group of about five boys sit on logs gathered around a campfire, all murmuring and smiling. In the background, there is a painted wooden sign that reads "Camp Cleary." Characters: JACK, ALAN, GEORGE, FINN, NOAH]

*Scene One, Act One*
JACK
Shut up, everyone shut up!
(The murmuring continues as the boys begin to take notice of JACK.)
JACK
I said shut the hell up!
The boys all fall silent and turn their attention to JACK.
JACK
Thank you. Jesus. Okay, who's going first?
(Most of the boys' hands shoot up in excitement, and ALAN, visibly the youngest of the boys, moans bitterly.)

ALAN

Jaaaack! I told you I didn't want to do this!

JACK

So leave, Alan! Just go back to the cabins if you're such a baby. No one's making you stay.

(ALAN looks warily up to the hill where a group of cabins is barely visible.)

ALAN

(Whimpering) But it's dark! There could be bears.

JACK

I goddamn wish there were bears so I didn't have to hear any more of your whiny bullshit. Stay or go.

(ALAN whines and shifts on the log uncomfortably, finally putting his head in his hands in resignation.)

JACK

Alright. Now. Who has a scary story?

(GEORGE's hand shoots up.)

JACK

A scary story, George. No one wants to hear about Louise. She's not even your girlfriend.

GEORGE

Is too!

ALAN

Who's Louise?

(The entire group groans in unison.)

GEORGE

Louise Fellbeck, the love of my life.

JACK

Christ.

GEORGE

You're just jealous because we're in love and nobody wants to touch your ugly ass!

JACK

Oh yeah, George? What base have you gotten to then?

GEORGE

What?

JACK

Bases, George—first, second, and third. What base have you gotten to?

FINN

You have to get to at least second to be really dating.

NOAH

That doesn't sound right, I thought it was first.

FINN

I think it's just frenching.

JACK

That is first base!

NOAH

Are you sure?

GEORGE

(interrupting)

We did first base!

JACK

Did not!

GEORGE

I swear! I stuck my tongue in her mouth and everything!

JACK

You're so full of shit, George.

GEORGE

Oh yeah? Have you ever kissed a girl, Jack?

JACK

I've kissed a million more girls than you, and I didn't even have to write any crappy poetry to do it.

GEORGE

It's romantic! You just don't understand the sensitive and complex female mind.

FINN

George is right, girls eat that shit up.

JACK

Whatever, girls are stupid.

GEORGE

Louise isn't.

JACK

Louise is hot, that's how I know she'd never date you.

GEORGE

Screw you, Jack.

JACK

Everyone's always mad at me, just because I'm honest.

NOAH

Guys, shush, do you see that?

(Noah points out toward the woods as the boys turn their attention to him.)

NOAH

I think it's a deer.

ALAN

It's probably a bear!

JACK

It's not a bear.

NOAH

It's definitely a deer. Should I get a rifle?

JACK

Are you kidding me, Noah?

NOAH

What? They teach us how to shoot for this specific purpose.

GEORGE
They teach you to hit targets under adult supervision, not to go shooting at shit in the woods in the middle of the night.
NOAH
It's 10:15.
GEORGE
We're not even supposed to be out here, technically.
NOAH
But think of what a hero I'd be if I single-handedly provided tomorrow night's dinner, free of charge.
FINN
Sure, we'll all have venison, and you'll get sent home for stealing a gun.
NOAH
My dad would be proud of me! He says I have a right to bear arms.
JACK
Your dad is psychotic.
NOAH
Democrats are making this country soft. He said that too.
ALAN
Which ones are the Democrats again?
NOAH
The men who kiss men, I think.
FINN
Your dad tell you that too?
ALAN
There are men who kiss men?
JACK
Maybe that's what George was doing when he thought he was kissing Louise. I bet it was pretty dark.

GEORGE

We didn't kiss in the dark. We kissed at the pond, during the daytime.

FINN

Did you read her a poem?

GEORGE

As a matter of fact, I did, and there's nothing wrong with that! Men can write poetry for the women they adore.

JACK

Since when are you a man?

GEORGE

Being a man is about your state of mind, not your age.

JACK

It think it's mostly to do with age.

FINN

Yeah, pretty sure.

GEORGE

I can't believe my mom made me come here. I hate summer camp.

JACK

George, you should be thanking us! We're preparing you for the real world. The people out there aren't going to be nearly as nice to you as we are. We're actually helping you.

GEORGE

(Glumly) Thanks.

ALAN

Noah, is that the Big Dipper?

(Alan gestures to an array of stars in the sky, and all the boys gaze upwards.)

NOAH

Yep. And there's Orion's Belt. And there's Cassiopeia.

GEORGE
(Dreamily) The queen.
NOAH
Yeah.
JACK
How do you know all that, Noah?
ALAN
Noah knows all the constellations.
NOAH
Yeah, my dad taught me.
FINN
(Sarcastically) Your dad sounds just chock-full of fun info.
JACK
Who is Cassiopeia?
NOAH
She was a queen who was punished for her vanity. She
chained her daughter Andromeda to a rock in order to save
herself from the monster that had been sent to destroy her.
JACK
(Inhales sharply) Her own daughter?
NOAH
Yeah.
JACK
Harsh.

# Coffee

**EUNICE CHOI**, Grade 9, Age 14. Manhasset Senior High School, Manhasset, NY. Shira Harwood, *Educator*

Buzzing dimmed yellow fluorescent lights, pushed-in blue chairs, wide eyes, silence. When it's last period, no one wants to focus on a video in health class on the dingy monitor, sitting on the scratched chairs. A fly lazily buzzes around the room, as the cold air from the slightly cracked open window blows on me. My knee shakes in anticipation when the words on the screen reflect on my wire-rimmed glasses. "Sexual harassment," it reads. A sharp drawn-out breath, red in my vision. I can't help but glance at the boy who held me down like gravity when I proclaimed that it was okay, that I was okay.

"Rape is defined as sexual intercourse without consent. However, we'll be explaining the concept without the usage of the word rape or sex. Let's think of it as coffee."

Instantly, confused sounds erupt around the room. The teacher yells at the rowdy teenagers to be quiet, as the cheesy MS Paint animation continues to play on, and I continue to shake my leg.

"Let's say you want coffee. You ask your friend if they want coffee, and they agree. You insert the coffee beans into the machine, and it's almost ready when your friend tells you that they don't want coffee anymore. Are you going to force them to drink the coffee because it's almost done? No, of course not."

The class explodes with laughter. I chuckle along anxiously, glaring at his brown eyes so hard I could've bored a hole in them. He's laughing along with one of his jock friends, who made some stupid joke I didn't catch. He doesn't dare meet my piercing gaze. Take a deep breath in, take a deep breath out. No one has to know.

"It'll be okay. It doesn't even hurt, and I have protection. Chill, you're not going to, like, become pregnant or something."

"I don't know, I'm not sure if I want to go through with this."

"But you told me yes before? And with that dress you're wearing—don't tell me you're not asking for it."

"Okay but—"

"Alright, let's say that both of you want coffee again. You're getting the coffee ready, and you can smell the scent wafting through the air. However, your friend has already fallen asleep in the time you've spent making it! What are you going to do? Pour the piping hot coffee down their throat to wake them up?"

Sweat is forming on my nose now, my heart beating quicker and quicker. The laughs seem distant now, almost muffled. Is it possible to feel like you're drowning when you're nowhere near water? I glance at the clock. Ten minutes to go until the bell rings. Only ten minutes.

"Alright, alright. I get it, you're some prude girl who doesn't want to fuck. I'll just find someone else, I guess." He turns to leave, and some form of desperation sinks inside of me, crushing me.

"No—I changed my mind. I'll do it. I mean, you can do it."

"Okay now, it's Friday. You both drank coffee together. Skip to Sunday. You want coffee, but does that mean your friend wants it at the moment because they wanted it two days ago? No. Even if they drink coffee often, that doesn't mean they want it daily."

Sweat dripping down my back. He says it feels good, but I can't feel anything. Still, I let out an unusually high-pitched moan, face down onto the cheap squeaking mattress. All I can see is red. He asks me if I enjoy it, my lips form the familiar word yes when all I want to say is no, no, no. He shoves his tongue in my throat but I want to spit it out, like I did with my broccoli when I was six years old with pigtails. Oh God, no.

"This all seems obvious, right? Why would you pour scalding hot coffee on someone because they fell asleep after saying they wanted coffee? Why would you make someone drink coffee if they changed their mind? Why would you assume that if someone had coffee the day before, or often, they would want it all the time?"

Why. Why. Why. I feel broken, but I know my limbs are intact with the way he moves against me. His name is in my throat, but the words I want to yell out are no, no, no.

"So why would you think the same way with sex?"

That night, I scrubbed and scrubbed. The image of the way he left reflected in my mind, as I pressed so hard as if I could erase my freckles that he touched, erase my memories. He told me not to tell anyone, because I "didn't want to be known as a whore." Not like anyone would believe me.

The video ends simply like that. It's silent, and the dying yellow bulb lights up the small room as the people around me blink to adjust their eyes.

"Are we all clear on this concept?" the familiar voice of my teacher booms.

"Crystal clear," his same calm, monotone voice echoes.

# Talk

**GEORGIA FLANDERS**, Grade 12, Age 18. Kearsarge Regional High School, North Sutton, NH. Lisa Cicoria, *Educator*

Here in the town of Fallingwood, we believe everyone's got their own special Talk. My grandma explained this to me when I was six years old, that every person had a Talk of their own, from the littlest child to the oldest senior citizen. It's what made people distinctive in conversation, she claimed. I had no idea what that meant, so I told her she was crazy and tried to run off, but she pulled my braids and made me sit down and listen.

Your Talk is really a simple concept when you get right down to it. It's sort of in the way you say things, the words you use and how you speak them. For example, my mom Talks like a good kitchen knife—quick bursts of rapid-fire dialogue, chopping words like vegetables. My dad could Talk a statue out of a marble block—his Talk's more of a hammer and chisel, wielded by the precise hands of an artist. Dad hammers his words out of the air, refining them carefully before using them, and when he's through, he's crafted a Venus de Milo of an argument. I suppose that's what makes him such a good lawyer.

Grandma's Talk is like an old car engine that won't start properly. Sometimes it putters along like it should, other times it stalls and spits so that you almost want to kick it to get it going again. When her Talk starts stalling, it's torture to listen to it. I asked her once why her Talk wasn't as pretty as Dad's—she is his mother after all—and she got all quiet.

"Your grandfather's Talk was like an auto mechanic, girlie. He's been gone ten years now, since before you were even a thought. Can't help it if I've missed a few tune-ups on account of that."

After that, she shooed me away, claiming I was tiring her out with all my questions. I had no idea what she meant at the time, but eventually I came to realize the truth about Talks—the ones belonging to people who were meant to stick together tended to be related somehow. Grandma Talked like a vintage car and Grandpa had Talked like fixing them. My sister Grace Talked like butterflies and when she brought home her boyfriend, we all knew he was going to be her fiancé someday because he Talked like flowers. That was Rodney Prewett, and he married Grace last summer.

Mom's and Dad's Talks were completely unrelated, and they divorced before I was old enough to understand why. Mom's word-chopping and Dad's word statues didn't fit together—in fact, they had a way of mangling each other. You can't make chopped vegetables into a statue any more than you can julienne slice marble with a kitchen knife, and although they tried their best, it just didn't work. Now Mom's remarried to the greengrocer and he Talks like an apple peeler, slicing away the skin around his words to get to the fruit of what he's saying. I think that marriage is probably going to last.

Dad never remarried. Although he tried to meet people and even attempted online dating—to Grandma's disapproval—his heart was still hung up on Mom. Although their Talks were totally incompatible, he couldn't get over her. Sometimes I'd catch him trying to imitate her Talk when he thought no one was around, hoping against hope that maybe if he learned to make his words sharp and quick like a kitchen knife, she'd come back to him. Grandma would watch him from her armchair and shake her head.

"Be careful, girlie, and see you don't end up like your father." Her Talk stalled for a moment, but she recovered. "If the Talks don't fit, the people don't fit. All that comes of trying it is hurt."

While Grandma's Talk was stalling worse every day, Dad was trying to change his, Mom's was hacking at everything, Rodney's was blossoming prettily, and Grace's was fluttering all over the damn place, I was getting into my teenage years and still had no idea what mine was. Sometimes, I sounded like Dad and could Talk a pretty decent clay pot even if I was no Michelangelo. Other times, I diced my words like Mom or puttered on like Grandma. I could even bloom and grow like Rodney or fly around like Grace. And it wasn't just those—I could Talk like people I'd only spoken to once or twice as well.

"You need to settle down and stop imitating everyone, girlie," Grandma spluttered indignantly one autumn evening when I went to visit her in the nursing home. "You're never gonna find your Talk if you keep this up."

She stalled then and didn't start again. Grandma started stalling longer and longer toward the end. A few weeks later, she stalled and rather than recovering, the engine of her Talk finally quit. We buried her next to Grandpa like she'd always wanted, out behind the old house. It wasn't until after the funeral, when I was sitting on the back porch and watching them lower her casket into the ground, that I finally figured it out.

I Talk like a mirror.

# Stovetop Glow

**MEGAN LUNNY**, Grade 11, Age 17. Central Bucks-East High School, Doylestown, PA. Colleen Rosini, *Educator*

Maria Sanchez must have been drunk when, in the middle of her mother's party, she pressed her whole palm to the burning stovetop in her mother's kitchen.

Or: This is the story the guests tell each other. Or: This is the story they tell themselves.

They stood in the kitchen, or in the dining room, or in the foyer. They held thin stems of bright drinks. They laughed about the weather, or their jobs, or their children. Tanya Sanchez floated among them in a velvet dress that she had bought three weeks in advance of today, her hair tied behind her in a tight knot. She was gray around the edges.

Tanya told her dinner guests that Maria was home from the city, and they said she looked very grown-up now, Tanya must have been proud. Tanya looked tired, but she smiled: yes, very grown-up. Very proud.

They agree, later, that Maria did not look at all grown-up. She was thinner somehow, sharper: Under her dress, her ribs were sewing needles. Her spine was knotted through her back. There were circles around her eyes as wide as moons; there was skin on her legs as pale as milk, bruises as small and dark as fingerprints. When someone said her name, Maria folded inwards; when someone laid a hand on her shoulder, she flinched.

It is agreed: If anything, Tanya Sanchez's daughter was younger.

They have trouble recalling what it is Maria did in the city. Someone thinks she was a waitress. Someone else says a stripper. They argue whether she was a schoolteacher or a receptionist. No, someone else says: Did you see those eyes? The way they moved around the room, eating everything. She must have been a thief, or an artist.

They agree that they didn't see her standing there looking for all the world like a wax girl, with wicks for fingers, trying to burn. They agree that they didn't notice that she was melting, or that she had parted her lips to swallow steam, or that water collected on her skin like pearls.

After all, how could they? Maria didn't scream.

But still. There was a moment before Maria reached for the stovetop, where Maria stared at the back burner, at the tea kettle with its heat smell and its steam, her eyes and mouth open. No one looked directly at Tanya's daughter: They watched through wineglasses or between fingers, heads turned away only slightly, as if they already knew what would happen.

Maria moved forward and lowered her hand to the stovetop; when her skin met heat, she did not flinch.

Maria's eyelids were lowered, her cheeks flushed: a face full of vapor, hair billowing in a cloud behind her. There was steam rising from her fingers, sweet-smelling, like the lemon soap in her mother's bathroom, or like the bread her mother had served with dinner.

Maria shivered. She was thin, and the steam was thick, and Tanya's daughter looked light enough to float away, to fall upward and into the air.

Minutes passed before Maria pulled her hand, the skin bright, away from the stove. They watched and thought that they shouldn't have been watching, that this—Maria, a steam-girl, burning like a saint or a martyr—was something holy and untouchable. But they watched anyway . . . and said nothing.

When it was over, Maria was a gasping puddle on the floor, her hand, still steaming, pressed to her chest. They flinched as though noticing her for the first time. They reached for her: Maria, what had happened?

They ran the kitchen sink. They found towels, bandages. They turned off the stovetop.

On the back burner, the tea kettle screamed.

When Tanya asked what had happened, they shook their heads. No one was sure. There was Maria, and there was the stovetop, what else? Steam and burning skin and a hollow-boned body, sagging on the floor, collapsing into itself.

Tanya crouched by her daughter. When they offered, she accepted the water, the towel, the bandages. She held up her daughter's hand. The skin was a bright, puckered red, and shone with fresh scars. They watched, and thought that gods and fires were not kind.

Tanya closed her eyes, chest rising and falling the way steam had tangled in her daughter's hair. Tanya and Maria sat to-gether on the kitchen floor, backs pressed to a cold oven.

Around them, the guests look away. Slowly, they return to their conversations. They hold cool glasses in warm hands, wonder how fire would feel against skin.

Before it is late, they leave, citing children at home or too much wine. In their cars, they grip steering wheels too tightly and remember Maria's face before she had even touched the stovetop: the way her sober eyes were wide only for a moment, already horrified of what she hadn't done.

# Gwen

**AMRITA VETTICADEN**, Grade 11, Age 16. Basis School-Ahwatukee, Phoenix, AZ. Michelle Dyer, *Educator*

The leaves slipped lazily on the breeze, flickering in and out between bushes and the warm canopy of the trees. Gwen leaned with sun-soaked languor onto the grass, the leaves circling and settling around her as if she were a forest sprite.

"So Anna, what do you want to do today?" she asked, a careless yawn escaping her lips.

You, I almost said, a reply she might have appreciated a year ago, when she was curled up in my bed with her bra on the floor and my fingers in her hair. A year ago, when our tongues would frequently get lost in each other's mouths as if we needed a little bit of the other to breathe. But today was Tuesday. It was July 3, 2017. The sun was out. And Gwen didn't fuck girls anymore.

The sunlight illuminated the gentle silhouette of her face, outlining the glowing coral of her lips. I wanted to run my fingers over those lips, that's what I wanted to do today. Reacquaint myself with her geometry, enjoy the mathematical sensation of having graphed every square inch of her body to my own plane of existence. Take a pencil and sketch. Fit another quick charcoal etching into the nooks and crannies of my consciousness. That's what I wanted to do. But Gwen wasn't my model anymore. Not my Dorian Grey.

She was sitting, but not for me. Now her chin tilted delicately skyward for the misshapen space between her boy's thumb and forefinger. Her paint-tipped porcelain fingers longed for the touch of her boy's hand. Her boy.

I did envy him. I hated how he reeked of Columbus, fabricating a universe for himself where Gwen was a pristine and virginal land ripe for his consumption. And I hated the thought of her playing along with it, the thought of her body rippling to someone else's touch exactly the way it had rippled underneath my covers at 1 a.m. in the hot darkness, our bodies tangled like moist summer vines.

Had she forgotten all the times I had caressed the immaculate curves of her skin and struck gold, the way a violinist reaches softly, expertly for a harmonic tone? Had she pushed to the corners of her mind the way my eyes covered her body with a fine dust of adoration? Forgotten who would immortalize her like Michelangelo immortalized David—if only she knew how to sculpt?

Several seconds had elapsed. Gwen turned toward me, her face a seductive mix of Fibonacci ratios and lost love. I could hear her question echoing in the stillness of the summer air. So I decided, finally, to answer. My voice was soft, when it came.

"I want you to remember."

**RACHEL ELLIOTT**, *Our Lady of Perpetual Production*, Printmaking.
Grade 11, Age 16, Piedmont High School, Piedmont, CA.
Gillian Bailey, *Educator*

# Sarcophagus

**ANNIKA CLARK**, Grade 11, Age 16. Home School, Andover, KS.
Andrea Clark and Murray Clark, *Educators*

The undertaker is quiet. The undertaker takes his time, and he takes yours too. No fanfare derails his gray fingers from the sterile process of wrapping a child typhoid victim in gauze and embalming her. This is what the undertaker does: the things that no one else wants to do. The undertaker scares even the most serious of men, with his cloth apron and elbow-high gloves all splattered with the afterlife. His skin is made of stains and scars.

I used to believe that the afterlife would be far away from this place, but the undertaker is a gothic bridge, a fatal reminder, a blood-splattered puzzle piece. Death is close, he reminds us; death is always nearby, he shows us. The undertaker unashamedly removes our organs from their homes in our peritoneum. There is no serous membrane to him, who dissolves all barriers between what it means to be here and to be gone.

Around the nineteenth century, my family decided that coffins should go out of style, sink away as they do with the sea burials of convicts. Gone was hexagonal, all clues at the shape of our bodies—tapered at the bottom to fit our final pose. My mother fits into no boxes, she disproves evanescence. My father refuses to dwindle, dim, or fade. The undertaker says to construct walls that protect and preserve until the ground covers us. We say, no. We say, more.

The undertaker is now the funeral director (we made him this way). He cries now, he lies now to grievers, he has advanced his chemicals. We will never dissipate or decay under his carefully calculated eternity. Now my family demands the jewel treatment, and we plea for restoration of limbs the undertaker would never have considered sacred. But he is no longer the undertaker, rather the funeral director, dressed in a paper suit and plastic shoes, and why is his hair so gelled, his handshake so familiar?

The funeral director asks us what kind of casket we would like, our choices split between luster and gaudy—all rectangular, all varnished, all covered in flowers, and none shaped like me (tapered at the bottom, slightly wider near the shoulders). Now the funeral director is actually the undertaker's grandson. This is truly the end of an era, the beginning of a new era, an era with no endings. He goes on about how every corpse —excuse me—how all the remains are jewels polished for a jewelry box, playing music that we've all heard before. Songs we've known since childhood, nothing new, nothing unknown or misconducted.

My family likes it better this way, how we draw out our grief like a bucket from a well in the town where we were born, refusing to see the fray in the rope. It is easier to turn away. It is more beautiful when you turn away, eyes cast on the indented grass footsteps that lead up to our graves.

# Ocean Eyes

**JESSICA LIU**, Grade 9, Age 13. Madison West High School, Madison, WI.
John Howe, *Educator*

*I.*

She finds it unfair that while she can't even touch a single soul,
the girl's eyes hold galaxies, infinite multitudes of swirling
stars.

They are ocean eyes, stormy eyes, eyes made for falling into
until you are swallowed whole by the brokenness they hold,
that wild glint that screams of driving at midnight with the
windows down and dancing in the pouring rain. And she wants
to sink into their depths, to be baptized in the swirling fragments of the girl's soul that drown her with those secrets they
hold, remake her with that pure light they possess beneath all
the darkness.

She sees those eyes in her dreams, devouring the broken
shards of her soul and spitting them out again, pieced together
imperfectly to somehow form something more beautiful than
before.

Of course, she always tries not to fall into those eyes. Because she's already bathed in holy water tainted with poison
and God's love, already soaked in the tears of angels. But in the

end, she always lets herself fall.

On her head, she wears a crown of thorns.

## II.

Every night, she prays. For what, she doesn't know. All she knows is what she has been taught, inhales words written 3,500 years ago and ideas that have ripped all her edges and fractured her light, then exhales silence.

But then, when she falls asleep, she sees the girl with the ocean eyes and the raven hair and the stardust freckles, and suddenly, she forgets that to love can be a sin, that those words she breathes in like oxygen should be her whole world.

In the darkness of her dreams, the girl strides up to her and tries to pull off the crown of thorns, but it digs into her scalp, refusing to let go.

And then she wakes up, hides behind a mask of empty words and walks on broken glass, and tries to forget about the girl with the ocean eyes, because somewhere, He is watching.

## III.

"How do you know God exists?" the girl with the ocean eyes asks, leaning in close on the rooftop beneath the stars, watching silently, disapprovingly. She smells of vanilla, stale cigarette smoke, and nights spent lying in the summer grass beneath the moon.

She closes her eyes. Breathes in beauty and a brokenness to match her own, exhales light that breaks through the darkness. Tries not to stare at those rosebud lips and the halo of moonlight around the girl's head that makes her look like an angel fallen from heaven.

"I don't."

It's true. But she has to have faith in something, for without faith, she would drown in the sea of thorns and water tainted with the promise of heaven that laps at her soul.

True, her faith tells her that her longing for the girl and her light is wrong, and every night, it shatters the light the girl lends her. And slowly, blood is starting to drip from the thorns on her crown.

In the end, she will have to choose. The idea of heaven, or the promise of love?

### IV.

To be gay is a sin, or so her mother tells her. But her mother is a rose stripped of its thorns, and she has been watered by those who find their truth clear-cut on the pages of a sacred book, not within.

One day, her mother sees two men holding hands, smiles that tell of pure love and joy plain on their faces. Her mother's lip curls in disgust, and she looks away, pulling her daughter close.

She remembers her mother's face, and her biting lecture afterward on the evil of homosexuality, how gays won't enter heaven. Because loving someone of the same gender is an abomination.

The idea of not going to heaven scares her, the idea of dying and simply ceasing to exist.

But the thought of not being able to love who she wants scares her more.

### V.

Their breaths mingle, and she can feel the pieces of her soul melding back together in a way that is imperfect, and yet somehow forms something more beautiful and strange than she can understand.

The girl with the ocean eyes shares breaths with her, and they lock gazes. And for a moment, the girl shares her pain, understands the weight of those words she carries on her shoulders.

"Why would God punish love?" the girl whispers, eyes searching her own.

For a moment, that crown of thorns lies next to them, forgotten. And in the girl's lips, she finds heaven.

## VII.

Her mother screams that she is going to hell, that she is a faggot, that she never should have been born, that she is an abomination and not a true Christian, that she won't be going to heaven.

Once, she would have prayed for her soul to be saved, begged for clemency for her alleged sins.

Now, she stands before her mother, and remembering those ocean eyes gives her strength.

Around her head, the crown of thorns cuts into her skin, but she no longer feels the pain.

# Transmissions from the Satellite Heart

**LEYLA EBRAHIMI**, Grade 12, Age 18. Flint Hill School, Oakton, VA. Tracy Peterson, *Educator*

I remember how you taught me to be kind. Kind was a feeling, you explained. Taste it on your tongue and unravel it, gracefully. We carried home injured butterflies and fed them sweet honey with our fingertips. We asked the great oak tree if he needed water, and we apologized to the grass as it would bend and crepitate beneath our feet.

We grew older. You wore cherry on your lips and danced with boys you didn't remember. You'd come home late at night smelling of acrid grapes and cigarettes. Your eyes would dance as you told stories of nights spent in little bars on big streets, filled with jazz and lust and zealous passion.

I asked you to take me to the edge of the garden, to ask the oak tree if he needed water . . . to feed the butterflies honey with your fingertips.

"Ask the grass for forgiveness," I said, as you ran to cars that waited at the end of the lawn. "Don't be silly, Siya," you replied. "The grass is not alive like you or me."

I told them you were sorry. I kissed the wide oak, and we cried together. You were forgetting us.

You told me colors tasted of rainbow, they melted into your hair and made you glow, made you seem holy and forbidding all at once. At night I'd listen to you, waging your own quiet war as you sang songs softly underneath your pillows, staining them with black mascara from nights you don't recall with boys you can't remember.

"Bite the rainbow," you said.

It tasted like nothing.

"It's wonderful," I told you.

I don't remember the way things changed. You got sick, and your hair that once grew raven lay in shambles at your feet. You cried, sitting on the floor of our bathroom, gripping it and shouting things.

"I suppose you've been waiting for this, Siya," you said. "You've always dreamed of being the prettier sister."

You turned green, hating me, throwing your food on the floor, cursing at my hair. "How does that feel, Siya?" you'd ask, pulling it. "It should have been you."

You spent your days watching the windows, watching the doors. Remembering suitors, laughter, dancing, cherry lips. You reached out to me one afternoon, bony, lifeless fingers that laced through mine. "Take me to the oak tree," you whispered.

We walked to the edge of the garden, slowly. I watched as you kissed the grass and stained the wide oak with your tears. I watched you smile, the wind hugging your godless soul and whispering forest-filling secrets into your ears. I watched you beckon to me, crying, melting onto the forest floor and screaming my name.

You swallowed the stars.

The trees.

The grass.

The butterflies we filled with honey.

You swallowed the edge of the garden until nothing else existed with the exception of you . . . of me . . . You were covered in forest, your blue eyes stars and your once-naked scalp plastered with moss. You looked beautiful.

# "Just Another Day in Hurricane City": Surviving Hurricane Irma

**ALEXANDRA BYRNE**, Grade 11, Age 16. Apex Friendship High School, Apex, NC. Kate Wernersbach, *Educator*

Most of humanity will never know what it feels like to be in a room of people certain of his or her imminent death. Jennifer Munro will never forget that feeling. After setting out on what was supposed to be a relaxing Caribbean sailing trip, Munro and her husband, Pedro Cuesta, found themselves caught in a living hell after Hurricane Irma and her nearly 200 mph gusts battered the tiny island of Tortola in the British Virgin Islands in September 2017 (The Weather Channel). After being summoned to dock in the Moorings Marina in Road Town, Tortola, with Irma looming, Munro and Cuesta took refuge in a small harborside hotel. "They told us, 'Let this be clear: This is not a hotel, this is now officially a hurricane shelter.'"

Munro soon realized the severity of the storm as the outer bands began to strike. "I really took notice of it and thought, okay—enough goofing around . . . Do I know where my passport is? Is that nearby? I have my raincoat." Munro and her husband took shelter in their top-floor room, devising a course of action in case the severe wind and rain rendered the room uninhabitable.

In their room was a cabinet that served as a closet. Hiding in that was plan A. But before long, the top of the cabinet had given way to an attic area, creating a suction tunnel. "It was a slow progression of the wind pulling and prying up the room." Even the ceiling began to fill with water, which Munro describes as "watermelon-sized balloons." As the wind and rain tore apart their safe haven, the next option was the bathtub. They created a haphazard shelter with a mattress leaning against the wall over them, although even this proved not to be particularly protective.

Suddenly, they heard an undoubtedly human knock at the door, which proved to be their frantic companions from the adjacent rooms. "They were yelling, 'Our roof is gone! Our roof is gone! We have to get out of here,'" Munro recalled, imitating the frenzy of their words. "The decision was to stick with our friends because they didn't have the greatest of health. We trust them, we came with them, and we will stick together." Although they had no specific destination in mind, Munro and Cuesta left the relative shelter of their room, dodging obstacles while bracing each other against the wind, holding hands, and walking single-file "like a human chain." Munro recounts her thoughts in those intense moments: "It seemed so ridiculous, almost. If they had not come to the door and said, 'That's it, we're leaving,' I would have never left the safety of my room."

After what felt like an endless haze of deathly gusts and pelting rain, "the wind stopped, the rain stopped, and the sun, for the most part, came out." Yes, the eye of the monstrous storm had come upon them, yet only for a short time. Rushing to find shelter once again, passing completely overturned catamarans in the marina, Munro and her group of eight combed the lobby and common areas of the hotel, yet found no place that would secure them for the latter, more ferocious, half of the storm. That is, until they encountered one of the managers of the marina, who led them to her room—one of the only ones remaining that was inhabitable. The room itself was pitch-black and flooded with at least four inches of water; Munro recollects that "there must have been already a dozen people in there."

As quickly as it had dissipated, the most powerful part of the eyewall ushered in new, more severe bands of wind and rain. Nearly twenty people were now crowded into two adjoining rooms. "That's when everybody's unique personalities and true colors all come out," Munro declares, grinning. It was a conglomerate of personalities, clashing and fusing, all reacting and accepting the uncertainty and provisional nature of their lives. "We had one girl who was doing a crying, sobbing confession of her life. She thought this was it, and she was going to confess: She's been a terrible person. And so she was going into this tirade. Then we had the other kind of a personality—another girl was just sobbing and crying and thought she was absolutely dying. And then, of course, we were trying to console her. We had a lady in the other room who was sort of sprawled out, sort of just shaking her head—not really saying anything."

Munro spent her time in this crowded, peculiar place working to alleviate the morbid imaginings of her counterparts. "My way to get through this was not to cry or to sob, but it was to spend my time trying to distract the people that needed to be distracted from this imminent death." She laughs, and notes again that death was not in her immediate thoughts in these moments. "The time just flew. Stuff needed to be done! People needed help! They needed to talk! I did my rounds of counseling and talking—being cordial and nice and personable—and trying to pull stories of their life."

She learned more and more about these nameless people during this traumatic time, deeming them "the ballerina" or "the girl on the bed"—their true identities remained unknown, yet the depths of their character lay exposed in the darkness.

The ballerina was sitting hopelessly in the dark, wailing confessions of her wrongdoings in life. "She was young. I told her that can't be true. I said, 'What do you do? You do something in your life.' She wailed, 'I was a dancer! I was a ballerina!' I asked her to show me her moves. It distracted her."

Finally, Munro struck a real chord in the ballerina—they both liked alternative music. "So I started to run her through all these alternative bands, and I would pretend that I forgot the lyrics to the song and I would prompt her—'Surely you remember that one with Eddie Vedder from Pearl Jam? How did that go?' She got it every time. For every rock star, she named him. For every lyric, she got it. Sure enough, she forgot her confessional tirade. She was so busy trying to remember all this—it was like she was on a game show or something."

The girl on the bed was a Belonger. "The islanders—they're called Belongers," Munro explained. "The poor gal was sprawled on the bed. I said how are you, how have you been? She said, 'Oh I don't like this, I don't like this at all. I don't like it.' And she's a Belonger. I said, 'Can I get you a shot of rum?' She's like, 'Oh yes, please!' I brought her a rum shot and we sat together."

When asked how her husband was faring, Munro responded, laughing, "I don't really know. I kind of think he was trying to poke his head out the door." The view out the door soon became visible to all as the storm died down, and the haggard group emerged from their battered refuge. "There was not a clear path to anywhere. There was just so much debris. It was a combination of smashed glass, corrugated metal that had ripped off roofs, downed palm trees, branches and leaves everywhere, [as well as] trash and garbage all over." The once vibrant, opulent, and lush island was now brown and bleak; few trees—and even fewer structures—were left standing. While walking through the rubble of Road Town, Munro "saw some people just walking around—like zombies. Most everyone was carrying a white bag full of everything they had at that moment. They didn't have anywhere to go."

Munro and her close group of ten were relatively lucky, however, as they were able to take shelter in the hotel's largely unharmed spa. For five days and nights, Munro and Cuesta called this home, creating a laundry system, cleaning the bathrooms, and storing food and drinks such as granola bars, coffee grounds, and water and juice. On the first night, emanating from whisperings that prisoners had escaped from the local maximum-security prison, the group established a rotation of guards. They created a small society within the spa, and Munro affirms that "it was sort of democratic." Each person had tasks to complete, thus each person took responsibility for the welfare of the whole. The British call this the "blitz spirit" —the formation of a community out of desperation and hardship; Munro describes it as "coming together one for all and all for one, and just doing it because it's the right thing."

As conditions began to deteriorate—with time ticking on their supplies of food, water, and fuel—many had their sights set on escaping the island. Several attempts were made by the group, including a boat hailed by the ballerina's firm, which stopped for exactly three minutes at their port before retreating to Puerto Rico. Munro was offered a spot on the boat under the condition she bring no luggage, but she declined after her captain refused the same offer. "We stayed with our captain.

[There were] just too many questions, [it was] too short of a time to make any crazy decisions."

The next day, an evacuation plan via airplane was arranged and approved by the now-present British Royal Navy, but it was abandoned minutes before the group would have set out for the airport. That night, although spirits were low, two Frenchmen led a sing-along in the common area. This turned out to be their last night in what Munro deemed "Hurricane City," as an evacuation by way of airplane succeeded the next morning. As she recollects that final night, she noted her relative good fortune that "people on their own [outside of the marina] didn't have any leader to hold meetings and briefings, they were just left with no roof, no place to go, and no water. Nothing. We had a community."

As Munro's plane rushed past the overturned planes and large heaps of metal on the runway, and flew high over the devastation below, she finally began to come to terms with the poignant and horrific situation she had escaped. "It didn't really settle in for me until I landed in the United States and I told what I had been through for the first time," she said. "That was the first time it emotionally hit me, and I broke down."

A ballerina dancing in the darkness, a group singing the bittersweet song of community in the midst of desperation: These are a few of Munro's enduring memories demonstrating how humanity shines its light in the darkest of situations. Now, let it shine its light on this tiny island and its people as they work to recover from a storm that was unforgettably devastating. Not only for the Belongers who have lost everything, but also for visitors to the island, like Munro and her husband, who just happened to be sailing by when nature's fury changed the course of their lives forever.

# The Coder's Code

**GEOFFREY BRANN**, Grade 12, Age 16. Ardsley High School, Ardsley, NY. Tara Bandman and Brian Gutherman, *Educators*

The professionals who hold your life, your money, and even your hair in their hands are regulated, licensed, and ethically bound to act in your best interests. Doctors cannot intentionally harm their patients, lawyers must keep your secrets, construction workers must abide by building codes, and any activity with the slightest degree of risk requires your signature. But there is one profession for which none of these rules apply. One that has access to your health records, your legal files, your financial accounts, your passwords, and even your baby pictures. A profession that openly boasts it can addict you, that is not regulated, has no ethical standards, no licensure, or even any entry requirements. One that, without your permission, has immediate access to your attention and your history, even while you read this: The computer professional. The geek. The hacker. The person in any country, without an office, for whom nothing is secret anymore. The app developer whose success is predicated on addictive technology. The fake news purveyor. The techie who reprograms Volkswagens so they need not meet federal emission standards. The dude who tells you your email is private or who works on the software that programs nuclear reactors. The big corporations that troll your data, insert cookies into your computer, monitor your shopping habits, and hone your Facebook feed. The company that takes ad money without vetting the source. The programmer who is programming you.

We know more about our Uber drivers.

The idea of a Hippocratic Oath for tech professionals and even amateurs has been discussed since 2002, when software engineers found themselves working on increasingly critical life functions. Data scientists became concerned that programmers, under pressure, might choose a quick fix to a software problem, creating a different issue, a new bug that would be harder to discern. With tech professionals in sudden demand, variability in skill was introduced. "Avoid risky fixes when the risks are unclear" seemed like a logical beginning to a necessary set of industry-wide ethical parameters. The risks, however, began multiplying at such an exponential rate, that the industry could not keep up with its own need for parameters—so none exist.

Today, the technology monoliths are well aware of the need for regulation. Google hired an ethicist, Twitter wrestles daily with issues of free speech, Facebook is assembling an Ethical, Legal, and Social Implications Board, and Apple hires moral philosophers. But the political and economic ramifications of random software intervention has far exceeded the lofty ideals of companies that prioritize profit. We are vulnerable to hackers, pirates, and anarchist engineers but especially to those big companies, which are turning their attention to the development of artificial intelligence. A pretense to morality, while their profits depend on our complacency, will not meet an urgent need for accountability.

A number of technology providers recently committed to creating new industry standards for the ethical development of artificial intelligence. Apple, Amazon, Facebook, Google, DeepMind, IBM, and Microsoft founded the Partnership on AI, recognizing that with innovation comes "new concerns for the effects of those technologies on people's lives." This "concern," tweets Elon Musk, could lead us into World War III.

Last month, industry leaders came out overwhelmingly in support of an eighty-three-page document developed by the London-based RSA titled "The Age of Automation," which suggests that artificial intelligence and robotics developers should sign a pledge to only develop technologies that benefit human society, providing that "Ethics training should be made a compulsory part of graduate computer science degrees, potentially culminating in a pledge akin to a Hippocratic Oath." Among the recommendations are for employers to co-create strategies with their employees, for tech companies to take a lead on drafting and signing up to ethical frameworks, and for the government to establish personal training accounts that could aid lifelong learning.

A code of ethics is certainly not the answer, but it could be the beginning of a conversation. A Code for Coders would go even further, as it is they who create the programs others exploit. As schools load their curriculum with tech and programming courses, they should recognize this and include ethics training, so the next generation will be equipped for the dilemmas the current industry is leaving behind.

How many seconds are you awake before you look at a screen? How many years will it be before a robot hands it to you? First, let it do you no harm.

# Through Grace's Eyes

**GEORGIA GREENBLUM**, Grade 12, Age 17. Grant High School, Portland, OR. Chris Hawking, *Educator*

Senior Grace Kowitch sits in her economics class taking steady notes about the dangers of credit card debt as her teacher, Dan Anderson, leads the class. Kowitch, who's wearing her signature cheetah-print leggings, a ruffled T-shirt and high heels, flips her hair away from her face and fiddles with her bracelet.

She is the only student in the class, or in any general education class in the school, with Down syndrome. But the congenital disorder that causes intellectual impairment and physical abnormalities hasn't slowed Kowitch down. And she doesn't take her education lightly.

Kowitch has taken almost all of her high school classes outside of the special education program and is more active in the school community than most high school students. Dance, choir, theater, swim team, basketball—nothing is out of Kowitch's comfort zone. She even mentors a younger student with Down syndrome on her speech and social skills.

But Kowitch is an anomaly among students with Down syndrome in the school and around the country. Inclusion of special needs students in general education classes is lacking despite the evidence that students gain better social and academic skills from it.

Having students with Down syndrome in general education enables students with special needs to learn higher material and helps combat negative stereotypes held against people with mental and physical disabilities.

Grant special education teacher Rina Shriki says, "It's beneficial for both students involved to be able to work together and get different perspectives from one another. When you have multiple perspectives, you're gaining more awareness of a situation. We need to be offering diversity as learners."

Although Grant does have an extensive special education program with three Intensive Skills classes for both medically fragile students and those with cognitive disabilities, there is still a lack of overlap between special education and general education. Most students are secluded in the special education classrooms hidden in the corners of the school.

While Kowitch's experience in general education classes has been mostly positive, it hasn't always been easy.

Locating a teacher who will accommodate her needs, keeping up with the curriculum and finding a place in a sea of students who learn differently than her have all taken a toll on Kowitch.

But despite the struggles, Kowitch and her parents say that inclusion is a vital aspect of special needs education.

"Grace's social and learning skills have been enhanced by the higher demands placed on her from being with typical students," says Kowitch's father, Art Kowitch. "The (general education) students also gain improved empathy and appreciation for difference from exposure to students with different learning styles and capabilities."

For Grace Kowitch, being involved in the school community

isn't about proving something—she just wants to be seen as another student. "I love school, and it is so nice to be in general education because everyone treats me the same as everyone else," says Kowitch.

\*\*\*

Kowitch was born two weeks early on September 21, 1998, to parents Art Kowitch and Kris Anderson and her older brother, Sam Kowitch. Minutes after she was born, the doctor told her parents that Kowitch had Down syndrome, leaving them scared for her future.

"We had a lot of worries . . . socially how the world would treat her and would be like for her," says Kris. "It was all new and different and was certainly something we never anticipated."

On top of this, her parents soon learned that Kowitch was born with a hole in her heart. At such a young age, surgery was a risky option. But they decided to go through with it, and after eight days, she was fully recovered. It earned Kowitch the nickname "Scrapper"—a family term for someone who is always up for a fight.

When Kowitch was three years old, her parents began exploring options for early education. They wanted Kowitch to practice her social skills from a young age. The family enrolled her at Early Intervention, a system of services that provided Kowitch with the initial help she needed through occupational and vocational therapy. The program, which doubles as a preschool, also helps individuals with physical and mental illnesses practice daily activities.

After full days at the preschool, Kowitch would come home exhausted. "She was like a sponge," says Kris. "She soaked up all the new material, and when she was on the bus, she fell asleep because she was so tired."

In 2004, Kowitch began kindergarten at Laurelhurst Elementary School in Northeast Portland. At the time, the movement to further incorporate those with disabilities into the general student body was in its beginning stages, and for the most part, instances of inclusion in the classroom at her school and across the district were few and far between.

Historically, all students with disabilities were isolated from their peers in separate buildings and didn't interact with general education students at all. In the 1950s and '60s, special-needs people were housed in state institutions, often with minimal food, clothing, and shelter. Physical and emotional abuse was also rampant throughout the sanctioned facilities, and needless to say, there was no form of education for the residents.

"A lot of the students I work with now, 30 years ago, they would have been in an institution, which is really scary to think about," says Megan Hull, a special education teacher at Grant.

By 1968, the federal government had supported training for just 30,000 special education teachers and related specialists. But educational opportunities were still lacking for the majority of students with special needs. In 1970, U.S. schools educated only one in five children with disabilities, and many states had laws excluding certain students from school.

Since the Individuals With Disabilities Education Act was enacted by Congress in 1975, that number has slowly started to rise.

Still, even just ten years ago, many teachers and parents were outwardly opposed to the idea of inclusion, and some still are today. Kowitch's parents remember how others complained that special education students would negatively impact their children's education, and teachers were frustrated that the district would put special education kids in their class without any support. "Certainly there were a lot of people who were not supportive of that, but we really were," says Art.

Cody Sullivan, who has Down syndrome, graduated from Grant in 2014. As a high school student, he took general education classes and helped out with the football program. His mother remembers facing similar struggles around inclusion in general education classes starting when her son was in kindergarten. "We have had to fight for it," says his mother, Anne Sullivan.

Kowitch also faced some hurdles when she began exploring different interests. In 2004, she wanted to take tae kwon do after watching her brother at practice. The instructor told her mom, Kris, that he didn't know if Grace "could do" tae kwon do. Kowitch didn't agree with him.

"I don't remember exactly what he said, but I felt bad for myself because I thought I can't do it," says Kowitch as she pumps her hand into the air. "I proved it wrong, so I kick butt."

Her older brother, Sam, says that people don't mean harm when they speculate about her capability to do something. "I think they just have a general misunderstanding about Down syndrome," he says. "Grace is capable of anything."

Kowitch came back the next week to take the class, and it wasn't long before the instructor changed his mind. She earned herself a blue belt in the third grade, and the instructor even gave her the "Student of the Month Award." "Grace decides she wants to do something, and she goes for it," Kris says.

*\*\*\**

That same year, Kowitch joined "Team Together," a club that helps bridge the gap between students with disabilities and those without through activities during lunch.

With the help of her private speech therapist, Kowitch was

paired up with a student at Jackson Middle School, Iris Tervo, who also has Down syndrome. Kowitch started mentoring her, mainly focusing on building vocabulary, making eye contact, and continuing a conversation.

Kowitch brings a vocabulary book that she received in seventh grade to the mentoring sessions and uses it to help Tervo practice her S's and L's.

They also take their mentoring sessions out into the community, going to Whole Foods to practice talking and making eye contact with the cashier as well as drinking, chewing, and swallowing food.

When her mentee goes into "shutdown mode," where she puts her head down, Kowitch tries to cheer her up.

"Iris is a bowl of fun. Sometimes I tickle her, and sometimes I draw a picture for her," says Kowitch. "I help Iris with her speech, and she helps me speak slowly too."

While Kowitch acts as a mentor for someone with Down syndrome, she herself realizes that she still has hurdles to overcome in her own learning process. After freshman year, Kowitch and her parents faced the reality that Kowitch can't just take any classes she wants. The teacher needs to be willing to adapt their curriculum, and their interactions with Kowitch must be hyperfocused. General class requirements sometimes have to be changed, which makes finding the right class for Kowitch increasingly difficult.

Additionally, the special education program is lacking resources. "Special education is a federal mandate but is not funded," says Mary Pearson, the director of the Special Education Department for PPS. "We are constantly moving things around to accommodate the highest needs."

This is partly why finding classes for Kowitch and others can be so difficult. Without funding, classes are cut and moved around frequently to make ends meet. "In the special education department, things never stay the same," says Kris. "Everything is constantly in flux, which is frustrating."

But through it all, Kowitch has still found her own ways to excel. And now, as senior year is coming to a close, Kowitch isn't slowing down. Between working at Wee Works Preschool for 1.5 hours per week, rehearsing for *Chicago*—the new school play she auditioned for and claimed a role as an inmate—and basketball practice, Kowitch is always busy. This year, Kowitch was also awarded the "best dressed" senior superlative for Grant's yearbook.

"It feels good," says Kowitch. "Because, you know, I am a fashionista."

Now, Kowitch is preparing to start her next journey and she is setting her sights higher than ever. She is waiting to hear back from the "Think College" program for students with cognitive disabilities at Portland State University. "I am ready to leave Grant High School and go to college . . . and travel the world, get an internship," she says. "I am going to do all the things that every other person is going to do."

# Paola Gonzalez: A Dreamer in the Land of the Free

**SHEHARBANO JAFRY**, Grade 11, Age 17. Bellevue High School, Bellevue, WA. Rocio Gonzalez, *Educator*

Running and panting, she eyes the finish line nearly 100 meters away. The wind rushes against her as her legs move rapidly across the gravel. Her long hair sways against her face. Inhaling and exhaling deeply, she focuses her attention on the finish line in front of her. Unwilling to give up, she knows that she will have to reach the end by herself. She no longer looks backwards or next to her, only forwards.

Paola Gonzalez is a junior at Bellevue High School. She joined track as a sophomore and became a rising star in her team, qualifying for district championships that same year.

"I qualified for track last year but couldn't go because I had to study for the AP World exam," Gonzalez said.

Gonzalez's love for running derives from more than the mere enjoyment of the activity. Much of her life, she says, has revolved around running. From one country to another, from one state to another, it seems as if she is in a constant race.

"Maybe one day, I can stay where I am and be happy," Gonzalez said.

Paola is not your usual teenage girl. What she has been through and continues to experience is difficult to imagine. An undocumented immigrant, Paola has been in a constant state of flux. As much as she wants to achieve her American Dream, she feels as if she is being held back, more so now than ever before.

On September 4, 2017, when she heard about the Trump administration's decision to terminate DACA (Deferred Action for Childhood Arrivals Act), her security, education, and aspirations "faded into the distance." That finish line seemed to be moving away from her, and she watched it leave.

"I was shocked and couldn't believe what happened," Gonzalez said.

However, she is just one in millions who are struggling to come to terms with what has happened. Like her, countless other undocumented individuals have to grapple with the insecurity that now surrounds them. They have to, as so many times before in our history, prove their worth to the people of the United States.

### The Beginning of the Race: Chandler, Arizona

Nearly 363 miles away from the Mexican-U.S. border in California, the city of Chandler sits in one of the hottest states in America, with temperatures rising up to 100 degrees Fahrenheit in the summer. With rolling hills and cacti-filled streets, this city is known as home by more than 230,000 people. For Paola, Chandler is especially important.

In 2005, the Gonzalez family arrived in the United States from Mexico. As foreigners, they were taken aback by the seemingly different environment they noticed. While in Mexico they found unfair education and healthcare systems, in the United States, they discovered an abundance of opportunities.

"Compared to Mexico, the teachers here actually teach, and there are resources in the classroom," Gonzalez said.

As her family settled into their new apartment in Chandler, they began to assimilate into American culture. In the process, they befriended other Latinos.

"We had close friends from Puerto Rico and other Latin American countries who were like family. We went to church with them and got together for Christmas," Gonzalez said.

Beaming, she relates how her connections with her first Hispanic-American friends continue till this day via occasional phone calls and social media messaging.

Nonetheless, the positive experience in Chandler was contrasted with the negative aspects. She understood the distaste that white Arizonians harbored for undocumented immigrants. In her parents' conversations and on the news, she remembers the political discourse that surrounded illegal immigration.

"People would talk about Joe Arpaio, and as a kid, I was afraid of him. I would always hear how he and other Americans hated Mexicans," Gonzalez said.

The infamous Joe Arpaio was the former sheriff of Maricopa County, the county where Chandler is located. He was nationally recognized for his anti-immigrant stance and use of racial profiling as sheriff. His name was feared among the immigrant population and reminded Paola about how powerless an undocumented individual is.

These events made Paola realize that in America, Mexicans are viewed as nothing more than "illegals crossing fences." She understood that people's perception of her identity pivoted around that one aspect and nothing else.

"In a way, the word *Mexican* became an insult," Gonzalez said.

Even today, that misconception permeates American society. Unfortunately, hardworking undocumented immigrants are generalized as only criminals who deserve to return to Mexico.

Although Chandler provided Paola with both enmity and acceptance, she began to treasure it as a home. Her love for the city became even more evident when her parents informed her about the job opportunity that was awaiting them up north. As she bid farewell to the apartment that she had settled in eight years earlier, she remained strong and looked at the future with unfaltering hope.

### Running: From Chandler to Bellevue

In a U-Haul truck traveling more than 1,400 miles, Paola sat in the backseat, listening to her "ambient kind of chill music." A music fanatic, Paola describes the powerful role that music has played in her life.

"Whenever I listen to music, I zone out and it becomes easier to focus on the moment that I'm in right then and there," Gonzalez said.

As the truck passed through towns and cities, the Gonzalez family made a temporary stop in Las Vegas, resting for a night in a La Quinta hotel. A day later, they began their journey once again. The people she met and the sights she viewed during that road trip remain entrenched in her mind.

"I saw the Hoover Dam and the Idaho city Twin Falls. And I saw snow for the first time," Gonzalez excitedly said.

Finally, when they reached Bellevue, Washington, they were astounded by what they saw: the tall Microsoft buildings, Lake Washington, and the iconic Space Needle. More importantly, they witnessed a greater phenomenon: wider acceptance.

Coming from Arizona, Paola was aware of how severe discrimination could be, and she prepared herself to confront the bias. Contrary to her expectations, Paola encountered mostly friendliness. There was none of the suspicion that she was previously accustomed to.

As they transitioned into their newly rented condo, the Gonzalez family sought to redefine their lifestyle and ensure that both their children could receive the best education. In 2013, Paola enrolled in Chinook Middle School and later Bellevue High School. She notes that although there is little discrimination, there continues to be a negative general perception of Mexicans.

"Mexicans are sometimes associated with being stupid in some form or another at school," Gonzalez said.

That is just one stereotype. Often, teenagers jokingly claim that Mexicans are illegal or rapists. Although these jokes are not intended to be offensive, Paola is disappointed that these misconceptions follow her. She thought that she would be able to abandon her status of that Mexican in Arizona, but she realized that she was wrong.

### Reaching the Finish Line: From a Dreamer to an Illegal

However much she tries, Paola is never able to forget "that dreadful Monday." The image of her parents' despondent faces continues to haunt her. When she was informed about the Trump administration's decision to terminate DACA, Paola's aspirations seemed to slip away. The faith that she maintained in America seemed to falter. The confidence that she had seemed to dissolve because of one decision.

"My brother and I started crying when we heard what happened. I couldn't help but think about our future and how we would get deported," Gonzalez said.

Many Americans cannot begin to understand the vulnerability of Paola's position. Her academics, job, and relationships are all at stake. As fast as she is, she cannot seem to outrun this situation. On top of that, she understands that she has little to no power in changing what has happened. Even then, she wants people to know the truth.

"While it may seem that America is ruled by the people, it really is not. If it had been, then this would not have happened. People like me would have been able to realize their dreams," Gonzalez said.

Before DACA, immigrants like Paola were unable to support themselves, as there were few laws that provided them with protection. The misery that undocumented people experienced at that time was unfathomable. When DACA was enacted, these individuals held hope in the new legislation because they were finally able to find that safe space.

Sadly, now, undocumented immigrants are forced into that state of worry once again. Moreover, Paola's dilemma is a difficult one to resolve, as it pits different political groups against each other. Opponents of DACA put forth that people like Paola are illegal, and that America has to abide by its laws. Supporters claim that these people are suffering, and the United States has the moral obligation to support them.

In the course of debate, however, what is forgotten is the importance of immigrants to America. As a result, immigrants are often harshly treated—the Chinese, the Jewish refugees, the Iranians, and the list goes on. At the end of the day, no one was benefitted; only harm was done. This is the same case today. Paola and millions of people like her are being rejected because they are somehow "illegal."

Unfortunately, when politicians label undocumented individuals as illegal, they disregard the contributions of these people to American culture, the education system, and the economy.

"People think we are coming here to steal people's jobs or 'take over.' Immigrants are not taking over. They are assisting; they are making America the country that it is," Gonzalez said.

American Progress reports that about 91 percent of DACA recipients are employed and are "outpacing the general population in terms of business creation." Moreover, "the 11.3 million unauthorized immigrants living in the U.S. today contribute $11.64 billion in state and local taxes each year."

However, those statistics remain inconspicuous in the grand scheme of things. Sometimes, what is visible is only the "illegal" status, nothing else.

Despite the remorse, anger, and so many other feelings she harbors, Paola remains steadfast. She knows that for change to be made, people like her will have to rise up against the opposition. That is why she plans to create or join an organization with her brother to ensure that undocumented immigrants are fully supported.

Not only her, but communities around the country have been stimulated by President Trump's action. Existing organizations like the American Civil Liberties Union (ACLU) have strengthened their position, while movements organized by volunteers are being developed.

For now, Paola's only hope is in the six-month period that has been allotted to DACA recipients before the law is put into effect. She aims to focus on what is important to her and remain optimistic for the future.

"I'm going to work hard. I'm going to keep doing what I have been doing and just hope for the best," Gonzalez said.

That is what she is planning to do, but she believes that it is essential for others to take action as well.

"People have to rise up against this. They have to stop things like this from happening," Gonzalez said.

Although a lot has changed in Paola's life, one aspect has not. Every day, she can still be seen stepping on the track field in her shorts and Adidas shoes. Although the race is difficult, she constantly runs to escape where she is, to go somewhere to find "some peace and calm."

As Paola nears the finish line, she takes a deep breath, closes her eyes, and shuts her ears from the noises that surround her. She runs as she has done countless times before.

Editor's Note: The names have been changed to preserve the anonymity of the interviewees.

# Fishbowl

**LUKE HERZOG**, Grade 11, Age 16. Pacific Grove High School, Pacific Grove, CA. Katie Selfridge, *Educator*

### Brief summary

Set in the near future, FISHBOWL examines the struggles of a space station's crew as they endure the view of a horrific nuclear apocalypse from above. With Armageddon as its backdrop, the novel centers on the gruesome murder of the crew's commander. Accusations fly. Prejudices surface. Tensions reach a boiling point. As paranoia begins to overwhelm the astronauts, and their conflicts begin to echo the destructive results 230 miles below, more blood spills. The whodunit in zero gravity becomes a question of who will survive.

### Expedition Roster

EXPEDITION 144:

Varun Duvvur (India) — Commander

Gabriel Florez (United States) — First Officer

Clifford "Red" Kaznach (Russia) — Second Officer

EXPEDITION 145:
Lesedi Naidoo (South Africa) — Commander
Dimitri Sadakov (Russia) — First Officer
David Dixon (United States) — Second Officer

EXPEDITION 146:
Yamato Sho (Japan) — Commander
Noah Abrams (United States) — First Officer
Eva Topfsky (Russia) — Second Officer

**Part One**
Unanchored

"We may brave human laws, but we cannot resist natural ones."
—Jules Verne, *20,000 Leagues Under the Sea*

For a week, the mushroom clouds left red dots on the astronaut's eyes—bloody phantoms dancing in his vision, taunting him. Closing his lids offered no respite from the torment. It had been four days since the bombings stopped, but the fires raged on. Abrams knew it wasn't healthy, taking every opportunity to spare a glance at the destruction below. But he couldn't look away. He was determined to bear witness to man's darkest hours. It was the least he could do, for the guilt was all-consuming. Floating above, watching Armageddon from the safety of their little palace in the sky. Abrams felt his stomach twist.

He was no less fascinated by his colleagues, 230 miles above the worst-case scenario. Each astronaut coped differently. Topfsky had retreated into her calculations, murmuring about fallout and wind patterns. She hunched over hastily ripped notebook paper so filled with equations and notations that she'd begun scribbling over previous ones. Discarded pages spiraled around her now, as if she was the star in her own solar system. Florez's diet had become irregular, to say the least. Caring too little to add water to powdered coffee and Kool-Aid, he scarfed them down dry—a nebulous cloud of brown and purple dust plastered to his face and following him about. Even Dixon's incessant toothy grin had long since been supplanted by a forlorn smile and furrowed brow, his light humor having descended into darkness and cynicism.

They passed over the half of the planet cloaked in shadow. The fires were more distinct against the black backdrop, flickering like torch bugs on a warm summer night.

Abrams was stirred by the sound of conversation, an almost alien concept as the hours passed, usually reserved for discussion of raw data and bleak hypotheticals. The buzz of consoles and the perpetual scratch of pencil lead had become white noise during their dark vigil for the human race.

"Ya spelled apocalypse wrong, darlin'," chided Dixon. The towering Texan hovered parallel to the engineer, face-to-face but upside-down. His goatee and shaved head made him look right-side up. Topfsky's eyes flickered, then she continued her scribbling.

"So I did. What's it to you?"

He shrugged. "Ain't the end of the world." Dixon smiled weakly. Topfsky looked disgusted.

"What are you working on?" Abrams turned his attention from the window and pushed against a bulkhead, launching himself toward the other two.

Topfsky sighed. "I'm writing an account of all that's occurred. The better question is—why aren't you?" Abrams's nose twitched. "What if ours is the only record to survive? Future historians might depend on our account. It might be all they have to go on."

Dixon raised an eyebrow. "Never had ya figured as a writer, Topfsky."

"Why so surprised?"

"Just always thought you wrote in binary."

She pushed him away, enough to send him floating backwards, and tugged a strand of hair behind her ear. "Jackass . . ."

Red appeared beside her, scratching at his chin and rolling his eyes as the Texan flailed for a handhold. The man's actual name was Clifford Kaznach. Dixon was responsible for the nickname—a not-so-subtle dig at Kaznach's Communist connections, though the man-child insisted he was referencing Clifford, the Big Red Dog. Nevertheless, it caught on. Abrams suspected that even the Russian had taken a liking to it.

"God, I'd like to sew his mouth shut," Red whispered in flawless English. He nodded toward the view of the destruction below. "And I wish we could draw the blinds too, you know?"

No, I don't, thought Abrams. "Yeah."

"So I was just talking to Duvvur," Red continued.

"Does the commander want another meeting?" Once the bombings had ceased, Commander Duvvur had called for a vote. Stay or go. Remain in orbit and hope rations—and the station itself—hold out long enough for a safe return, or attempt a landing on a toxic world. They had long since lost contact with Earth; the choice was theirs and theirs alone. For all they knew, the planet was too. The debate was long and intense. Opinions were evenly split. In the end, Duvvur cast the deciding vote. They would stay.

# The Mexican-American Dictionary of Familial Communication

**ISABEL ESTRADA**, Grade 12, Age 18. South Carolina Governor's School for the Arts & Humanities, Greenville, SC. Scott Gould, *Educator*

**Es·tú·pi·do. noun.**

It's what your parents call your brother when they find his bedroom empty early one school morning. Most of his belongings are still there. The Tootsie Roll coin bank he had since he was young, his hair gel, the picture of his grandfather hanging on the wall in a wooden frame. His dresser is almost completely empty except for a few shirts spilling out of the half-open drawers. You can tell he left in a hurry. As if he made plans to leave but forgot. You're young and still learning Spanish when you first hear this word. It means "how could you do this to your family?" It means "you've made us look bad." At church, your father tells everyone who asks that your brother is staying with an uncle in Georgia for a while. He doesn't use the word then.

### *Fe·liz. adjective.*

Your sister, Yessica, has lived in Houston for over a year when she calls your mother to tell her that she loves another girl. The house feels hollow in the days following the phone call. The one time you bring it up to your mother, she swears it is a practical joke that your sister is playing on her. When Yessica was in school, she was at the top of her class. She was involved in clubs and team sports. She was the ideal daughter. The first of the family to go to college, their pride and joy. The daughter they always compared you to when you messed up. When Yessica moves to Houston, she falls in love with a girl named after a '70s rock star. She told you, then your other sister, then a few months later, she called your mother. When she comes home for Thanksgiving, she explains to your mother, *"Estoy feliz."* She's happy for once. That night, your mother confides in you that she does try to understand. That she does try to see how two women can be happy together, but that God created man and woman for each other, and Yessica can't really be happy with her girlfriend. That when she was a kid, making her parents proud is what made her happy. Your mother says the kids of this generation don't learn their parent's values like she did. She says that in her day, you didn't hear about two girls liking each other because they kept it to themselves, but in today's time we have to say everything. After that night, she rarely talks about Yessica except to recount stories of when she was small. When they talk on the phone, my mother does not ask how her girlfriend is. Instead, she says things like, I hope you do find a good man one day. She no longer compares the two of you.

### *Triste. adjective.*

One Saturday morning, you're in the kitchen with your mother. She is making breakfast and you are sitting at the kitchen table and the sun is slanting through the large windows. Both of you are laughing at the hosts of a Spanish morning show who spend their time gossiping about celebrities. When the program goes to commercials, your mother silences the TV. She says the loud voices give her headaches. It is quiet for a while before you tell her that something has been on your mind for a while now, but she doesn't ask what it is, just says hmm? In broken Spanish, you tell your mother that you feel sad a lot. *Triste.* That you don't feel like eating lately or that you don't look forward to big holidays or your birthday anymore. And that your hair has been falling out a lot more and that's probably why the shower drain clogs so much lately. You trace the lip of the mug in front of you with your forefinger, and the room is silent except for the flipping of the tortillas on the comal and the sizzling of the eggs in a pan. You look up at your mother, but she is still focused on the stove. After what is only a few seconds, but feels like long minutes, she says, "You're sad? I was sad when I didn't have any food to eat as a child. *Mija*, please, we all go through times like these. We just have to pray."

### So·por·tar. verb.
This word is a false cognate. It sounds like the word *support*. Support: like your father telling you about his family's history of depression and that he understands. Like knowing it's okay to be like that. Or like finding help for you. Or like welcoming your sister's girlfriend to the family. Like whatever would have made your brother stay. Like talking, asking him if something was wrong. In Spanish, this word actually means "to bear, to endure." It means not everything should be said aloud. It means America has made you too dependent, too reckless, disobedient. It means there are some words you have yet to learn. That you have a different definition.

**YOO SUNG LEE**, *A Luminous Night*, Painting. Grade 11, Age 16, Lambert High School, Suwanee, GA. Yoonhee Chung, *Educator*

# Jones Beach

**KALLEY HUANG**, Grade 12, Age 17. Hunter College High School, New York, NY. Caitlin Donovan, *Educator*

The first time you read English is in a tiny Dora picture book with big Comic Sans letters and one-dimensional characters. It seems worthless, but your parents buy it for you anyway. They buy you tens of these books even though they sometimes can't make rent, so while Swiper never seems to learn his lesson, you become fluent in the art of stealing a language and making it yours. The first time you speak English is much earlier. Your parents force out unfamiliar, colonial, and Anglicized syllables so that, in theory, you learn this tangled language together, but learning a new language at three and learning one at thirty are very different.

You run with it, and it sets you on fire. Your lungs burn. You burn when you translate for your parents. You have played both the role of the uncomfortable (for the teacher and your-self) ESL student and the interpreter since you were four years old—God, imagine still playing with knock-off Barbie dolls and already being that much more fluent in English. You burn when you write. There are emotions, thoughts, and ideas that want or maybe need an escape that you can't provide yet. There are things in your head that may never escape. You burn at the beach, which your father hates. He drives you there, though he refuses to even exit the car. You think the first smell of the salty ocean air is possibly the best part of going to the beach.

So you and the rest of your family go to the beach. You build sand castles with your little brother, trying and failing to construct a moat. You try, though, which is what counts. You wonder if your parents share the sentiment—probably not. If you try, succeed. You don't tell your little brother, but you personally think your time would have been more successfully spent working on the towers. But you move on, always looking for more. Together, you pluck seashells and seaweed from the sand, plastering them on the walls in an attempt to stabilize them. In the end, it seems like the sand castle is missing something, but despite your little brother's insistence, it is not the moat. Eventually, it becomes difficult to enjoy yourselves, despite the gentle embrace of ocean air and warm sunlight. The sand gets everywhere, and the idea of your father sitting alone in the car annoys you, nagging like squawking seagulls and picking until your wounds are raw.

You slink back to the car, and your father asks if you went into the ocean with an unnecessary amount of urgency. He is a stick in the sand, and he remains one until your parents accidentally leave a manila file on the table. Don't open it; curiosity killed the cat. But satisfaction brought it back, so, in a flash of pubescent rebellion and stubborn curiosity, you open it. "[REDACTED] seems to be at risk for mental illness, particularly depression and post-traumatic stress disorder. This predisposition for mental illness would be dangerously aggravated by the deportation of his wife, [REDACTED]. The stress of losing his wife and raising their six-year-old daughter, [REDACTED], by himself is life-threatening. It would be irresponsible for the state to deport [REDACTED] and to separate this young family." Jeez, how does anyone have a family whose names are all [REDACTED]? Can your name even be all caps and bracketed?

Years later, you discover your parents crossed the Atlantic and entered America with nothing but dreams—your mother on a plane, your father on what may have been the oldest, weakest boat in the world. He probably thought he was going to drown and die, so he probably only recalls unaddressed trauma at the beach. The beach has bonafide American beauties with blonde hair and tan skin, and you are jealous—God, imagine having so much time that you spend the day on a beach in the nasty sand, under the burning sun, by the deadly waves. He probably hates the beach and swimming because of that. You guess; you don't know. You don't talk—can't talk—with them because you're fluent in only one Chinese dialect while your parents are fluent in three. But they're fluent in neither English nor emotion, but who has time for emotion when you're starving, homeless, and in constant danger of being deported? They probably didn't. You guess; you don't know. Who has time for emotion anytime?

They both work hard for you, which is how to show real love. You don't need anything else. Both brown hands in the dirt means they don't need the beach to be brown, beautiful, ugly. You don't know how to tell them that you love them, hate them, love them—as in you literally don't know how to say love in your first language. You don't know if they love you or hate you. You don't know how to tell them that you feel both ways constantly. You don't know how to tell mama you want to scream for her because she deserves so much more than you, and you don't know how to tell baba he can go to the beach and swim and be happy and free.

# Last Words

**LAILA SHADID**, Grade 11, Age 16. Buckingham Browne & Nichols High School, Cambridge, MA. Sarah Getchell, *Educator*

I read his books, his articles, absorbing every word in search of his identity, in search of mine. I run my finger across the page, desperately trying to grasp the meaning of each adjective, noun, and verb, craving his vast knowledge in the mechanics of a good story. His presence leaps from every molecule of black ink, and a familiar warmth cocoons me. I can almost feel the prickle of his peppered gray beard on my cheek, the sound of his voice floating through the telephone from a war-torn Middle East, the faint smell of Mediterranean spices imbedded in his wool scarf.

But how could I be attracted to the art that killed my father?

My mother watches as I write, often commenting on the way my brow furrows just like his did, how my adjectives carry an uncanny resemblance. Having known my father for years prior to my existence, she watched him develop into the two-time Pulitzer Prize winner he became. She knew the sacrifice and joy that writing was in his life, knowing that it was the only thing strong enough to take him away from her and me, his three-month-old daughter, and into the Iraqi war that ultimately led to their divorce, his life in the Middle East, and his death.

As a child, I remember a house in Silver Spring where the lawn was always manicured and the beds always made. A place where my mother and my father danced in the living room, spinning me around in their arms. A place where we came together, only to fall apart.

When smoke poured from the Twin Towers on September 11th, it drifted through our TV and soiled the clean air around us, suffocating our suburban home. My father knew what this meant—he had to go. He was the only one who could tell the real story.

Off he went to the Middle East, returning a few months later with a hole in his left shoulder where the bullet of an Israeli sniper had pierced his skin, entering his back, and barely missing his spine. On the verge of paralysis, he described the sky in Ramallah that day as cemetery gray.

My father wanted us to go with him to the Middle East, pick up our life in Maryland and live as a family between war-torn countries. My mother wanted to pursue her career as an obstetrician, in the safety of the East Coast.

I cried for my daddy. I cried because at nine months old, I didn't know where he had gone, I didn't know when he would come home, and when he did, I knew it wouldn't be for long.

And now I wonder: Is this where he would have begun the story of his death? Or possibly with the phone call from his boss ten years later, forcing him to travel to Syria, telling him that it was risky, but there would be people there to help them cross the border. A plan that quickly fell apart when a pack of dogs began to chase my asthmatic father and the photographer accompanying him, John. He wanted to rest, to catch his breath, but John urged him to keep going, they would be safe soon, so he did what he did best: pushed his limits, limits I imagined were infinite.

Maybe he would have begun with the last puff of his army green inhaler, describing his struggle to breathe in the dusty air around him, kicked up by their final attempt to escape the daunting howls of German shepherds. The feeling of snakes coiling around each lung, slowly constricting each capillary until release was not an option. Grabbing his weakened heart, collapsing on the side of a dirt road, the imprint of his valiant body in the hard earth, John's immediate efforts to perform CPR that would prove unsuccessful, the ratio of 30 compressions to two breaths, his chest inflating with empty air, deflating with despair. He would have illustrated his last breath in such detail, that it would be yours too.

When all hope was lost, John lifted my father's body from the ground and over his left shoulder, just like Daddy did when I was a little girl. I would scream and giggle as the blood rushed to my head. "Sack of potatoes," he called it, careful not to drape me over his wound. "Again, again!" I would beg.

John walked for miles, reaching Turkey with news that destroyed my world.

\*\*\*

I believed him when he told me he was not going to die, when he told me not to talk like that, not to think those thoughts. At ten years old, I grasped his words tighter than the computer I held on my lap, his unshaven, two-dimensional face staring back at me with love, pain, and guilt. I believed him when he did not believe himself, sitting at the desk of a seedy hotel room in Cairo, a revolution exploding outside in the hot Egyptian air.

And now, less than a year later, I was asking myself: How did I get here?

How did I get to the bathroom floor, screaming on my hands and knees, pressing down on cold tiles through inconsolable tears? How did I bring the phone to my ear and listen to my grandfather cry? How did I fall asleep that night? Was it to forget for a few hours? Was it for that moment of pure oblivion before my eyes opened and I remembered the truth?

He was supposed to Skype me that day and tell me about his trip to Syria. The villagers he danced with, the children he spoke to, the hospitality of the woman who offered him tea on her budget of a dollar per day. We were supposed to review the latest Arabic homework, Ms. Maha would be angry if I didn't do the assigned reading, and I knew I couldn't complete it without his help. He still hadn't heard about my latest project in fifth-grade science, Ms. Brown's praise of my short story, or the A+ on my math quiz, and now he never would.

Suddenly I was flying over the Atlantic, making the same trip I had made for the first time last summer, except this time, he wasn't there to point out Beirut's clustered coastline from the tiny window above. This time, I couldn't hold his hand as the plane touched down on the land below.

\*\*\*

In Marjayoun, the sky was cemetery gray. The house he rebuilt stood just as I remembered it, made of the same stone my great-great-grandmother touched as a young woman before escaping to America, her hands the same size as mine. I walked along the garden he had loved like a third child, always returning to Cambridge with stories of a new harvest or a bag of olives for us to pickle. I stopped at my olive tree, almost my height now, and reached out to glide my fingers along its silky bark. Zeytoun, I whispered, repeating his words into the fragile leaves, the language of my ancestors rolling off my tongue.

He wanted to be buried under the fig tree.

It stood taller than the rest, towering over the garden at one hundred years old, stretching its arms out wide, protecting everything below. I took the shovel and helped dig a narrow pit to hold his ashes. It was hard to believe you could fit the biggest personality into such a small hole.

Moist soil was scooped onto the thin white bag until every inch of the bright cloth disappeared into senselessness. They placed stone tiles on the dirt in a perfect square, perfect just like him.

I kneeled down at the edge of his grave and let my tears wash the dirt from my ancestors' stone.

"Goodbye, Daddy," I cried, lifting my head toward the sweet fruits above. "I love you."

\*\*\*

Daddy used his words to say "I love you" back, write my birth announcement, and tell his ancestors' story where his guilt was uncovered. He called for me to be in his articles, books, and stories, but the choices he made to be absent in my childhood did not allow for my presence. Each word he wrote pulled him farther away from me—across oceans, Bedouin villages, and ancient olive trees—but without them, he would truly be dead. Daddy wrote to tell me stories I could not understand then, to make sure I knew where I came from, to understand the Arab Spring, and most importantly, his legacy. Part of him died with every story, but each gave him a reason to live.

I understand now that he wrote for the world that I was a part of, the world that I would come to recognize as my identity. He wrote my world, he was my world, and now it is my turn to write for this one. I call for him to join me in this journey, to live through my writing and his forever, because how can you die without having said your last words?

# My Grandmother's Bones

**ANANYA GANESH**, Grade 10, Age 16. Westminster School,
Atlanta, GA. Jennifer Dracos-Tice, *Educator*

I dreamt of my bones every night. I pictured their smooth and
slender white surfaces, cloaked in layers of skin and muscle,
like chains of slumbering reptiles, linked by the inevitability
of their common fate. I waited patiently for one of them to
rouse and stretch, hoping the glorious cascade would shake the
others out of their stupor. Many nights I lay in the dark listening intently for the slightest creak of their awakening, willing
them to reach across and lock heads and tails.

They slept.

I'm not quite sure of the precise moment when I went from
being delightfully petite to just plain short. Perhaps the summer after which everyone returned to school, their generous
bones bestowing upon them the inches I so deeply coveted.
Mine had hibernated all summer. I tried to ignore the whisper
notes of taunt floating in the air wherever I went. Even the
orange tree in our backyard, laden with luscious spheres of
sunshine, seemed to mock me. My father had planted the sap-
ling when I was a toddler. My parents continued the practice
of their homeland, believing that as the tree grew, so would the

child. My mother watered it faithfully every day, praying to the Tree Gods to hold my hands and raise me up tall and strong just like them. They simply ignored her. My bones just couldn't keep up with the orange tree.

My mother's days were consumed with percentiles and growth charts. "Late bloomer, perhaps," people quipped. My father worked into our conversations names of accomplished people while feigning surprise at their incidental shortness. "Bones have no business being late," I complained to no one in particular.

That summer, we went to see Paatti. It was the summer I learned why the Tree Gods had failed me and why it didn't matter anymore.

"We're going to see Grandma," announced my father, his voice muffled with longing. My heart ached for him. I could not imagine not seeing my mother every day, not cuddling up to her bosom for five more minutes of sleep, not spilling my adolescent woes into the crook of her neck, soothed by her scent of ginger, garlic, and sandalwood soap. I hadn't seen my grandmother since I was a toddler, my forgotten memories of her sometimes surfacing like fireflies out of cinder.

We reached Paatti's house early in the morning. The heady petrichor of early monsoon showers caressed my nostrils as I stepped out of the car. I watched in awe as the neighborhood women started their day casually creating complex geometric patterns of rice flour loops and circles outside every doorstep to entice the Gods of Prosperity. Far away, the intermittent scratch of grass brooms sweeping across concrete sidewalks woke reluctant residents.

I almost didn't see her open the door.

My eyes, searching for lost sleep took a while to find Paatti. But when they did, the air froze in my lungs.

Hungrily, she gathered me into her arms. My head towered above her disheveled sea of gray. I looked closely as she released me to hug her son, barely clearing his waist. Sparkling, serpentine, gold chains were lost in the folds of her stunted neck. Paatti's bones, like mine, had changed their mind halfway to adulthood. I couldn't distill the rainbow of myriad emotions that swept through me. Even as I felt somewhat relieved that it wasn't entirely my failing, I tasted the acrimony of rage and disappointment at the back of my throat. There was my grandmother—the unmistakable reminder and cause of my Lilliputian fate.

I felt an urgent need to let the whisperers know. It wasn't my fault. It was my destiny. My vigil had ended.

I woke to the sound of Paatti's voice—honey flowing over smooth stones. She was teaching my mother the secret to making perfect *poli*—my father's favorite breakfast. Perfect circles of flaky pastries sat in a sticky syrup of sugar and loneliness. Skinny rivers of hot clarified butter crisscrossed the polis. Paatti insisted on feeding me, her slender fingers deftly pulling the layers of poli apart until the bruises of separation were all that were left. I took a bite and the poli melted in my mouth, tasting of the fear of another farewell.

Later that afternoon, Paatti took me to the temple. She had draped a bright-red silk saree, spires of golden thread woven into an intricate filigree of temple towers and elephants. Her diamond nose ring caught the light and spewed fire as she turned her head, strings of orange jasmine in sharp contrast on her gray mane, the middle of her forehead sporting the perfect vermilion circle. Paatti looked resplendent and . . . short. The lump in my throat was back.

"For you," she said, handing me a matching skirt set. Made of the same bright-red silk fabric of her saree, twin golden elephants. She had sewn them herself. I tried on the skirt, and before I could speak she squealed, "See how it fits perfectly. You have my bones!" My eyes brimmed with regret threatening to spill over.

Heads turned as we walked to the temple—matching visions in red silk and jasmine strings. "My granddaughter," Paatti introduced me as pride lit up every tired wrinkle on her face.

Outside the temple sat rows of people—young, old, children, newborns, missing limbs, missing voices. In front of each one of them lay steel bowls into which the temple goers flung money from afar. Disease had maimed their bodies and tarnished their souls. Even as people avoided looking at them, afraid their misery was contagious, Paatti sat down amidst them. I worried that the elephants would lose their gold. She fed the little ones the poli she had packed in fresh banana leaves and chatted with the ease of familiarity. I watched mesmerized as the children started to play around her—some lying on her lap, another one playing peek-a-boo with her billowing saree, all of them soaking in her radiance. After a little while, she rose to go inside the temple, and the children, like mutilated and blind mice, followed their enchanted piper until the doorstep.

And then we went into the temple to pray. I hoped she wouldn't ask what I had prayed for.

I wore a new skirt every day—six lustrous yards of blue, pink, and yellow silk sprayed with gold and silver spires, the elephants always golden. We walked to the temple with our clothes and bones perfectly matched. When we returned home, the elephants on Paatti's saree were always speckled with the dusty remnants of the arenose temple street where the children played.

On most days, after lunch, my parents left to catch up with friends and relatives. Paatti and I were alone. She made me sit on the back porch, facing the jasmine tree. In her hand was a bowl of coconut oil—"the elixir for my tresses," she insisted. "If it soaked enough, could it make my bones grow?" I wondered. Her long, bony fingers delicately parted my hair as she carefully coated each dark strand. My thirsty scalp gorged on the rich oil. The intoxicating scent of jasmine in the air and Paatti's fingers rhythmically massaging my scalp in slow circles was about to lull me to sleep.

That's when the stories started. Hesitantly at first, gentle waves playfully lapping at my feet—testing and teasing. One step at a time, Paatti held my hand as we started to descend to the depths of her heart. At every step, a different, younger, Paatti met me and took me further. The child, orphaned at eight, raised by aunts and uncles, a poverty-stricken childhood—no golden elephants or silver spires, the teenager forced to end her education abruptly and marry a man she hadn't met before. The hint of a blush disappeared in the ridges of her chestnut wrinkles. Then her eyes darkened—the color of grief-stricken clouds. Her words faltered and her voice began to crack, unable to bear the weight of the story that followed— of losing her first born, and second and third . . . I wondered if her heart bled with every beat, squeezing out the excess sorrow it couldn't hold?

Sirens screamed in my head to drown the question threatening to escape.

"This is not the time," my mind chided.

"Did it bother you . . . I mean . . . were you ever unhappy . . . because you are sh . . . sh . . . s-h-o-r-t?" There! I said it. The words slipped out of my mouth slick as the oil on Paatti's fingers, before I had the chance or sense to chew them down. Her laughter sounded like my mother's brass pots tumbling over—the ding-dong of temple bells. "Short?" Surprise coated the chestnut ridges on her face.

"Do you think I am short?" I didn't answer, but I was sure she could see the trail of pain starting to form on my face.

"I was one of the taller girls in my village. And beautiful too!" She cradled my face with her hands. "And you have my bones. But the problem is," she swatted an imaginary fly with oily hands, "your bones don't know yet that they have left home."

Her words pierced my heart and plunged to my soul. No one had said that to me before. The jasmine branches swaying and nodding in the evening breeze agreed with Paatti. Her words, bounced around in my mind, knocking down the cobwebs I had been collecting for years. In the new vastness of my mind, I realized slowly that there was nothing wrong with my bones; I had merely forgotten where they had come from. How tall I grew was as much a part of my heritage as the big copper pot of turmeric-colored curry my mother cooked every Sunday. I had unfairly pitted my bones against counterparts of a different league. I had assimilated so completely and was entrenched so deeply in the world I was born into that I had neglected to hold on to the world I had come from. If I had learned to embrace this fact earlier, perhaps I could have saved myself from years of heartache. Like my kohl-lined dark eyes, like the tendrils of my jet-black silky hair, like my skin the color of melted caramel, my bones were fulfilling their destiny.

I had inherited my grandmother's bones. I hoped I had inherited the tenderness flowing from her heart. I wished for her indomitable spirit.

I never dreamt of bones again.

**KYLE BROWN**, *Scatter Brain*, Digital Art. Grade 11, Age 16, Reno High School, Reno, NV. Brian Bolton, *Educator*

# Truths I'm Trying to Ignore

**SOPHYA GIUDICI-JUAREZ**, Grade 12, Age 17. Miami Arts Charter School, Miami, FL. Jen Karetnick and Ariel Lewis, *Educators*

I am five years old. I do not understand my homework. English still sounds a little too rough around the edges. My mouth wasn't built to accommodate this blocky language. I struggle holding a conversation but make friends anyway. My teacher told me that if we had any questions, we could ask our parents. When I do, my mother holds the paper away at arm's length, as if it is insulting her. She grips it between pointer finger and thumb and squints, pretending the problem is her eyesight, not her understanding. She is embarrassed. She hands the paper back to me, and tells me that as long as I try my best, I will go so far.

I think of my father, and how I'd ask him for help if he was home. He woke up before I did this morning, and he won't be back until after I go to bed. Sometimes I can hear his boots echo through the small apartment, late at night when I'm supposed to be asleep. When he comes into my room, I open one eye and peek at him as he kisses my brother and I goodnight. He always knows I am awake.

"*Duérmete*," he says. So I do.

***

I am eight years old. I no longer need help with my home-work. I haven't asked in years. My mother needs me to help my brother in school. I talk to his teachers and translate his read-ing questions for my parents. I show up to every open house with them, sit in on important conversations, and translate our mail. I know more about taxes than I need to.

I want to be in gymnastics, but when I tell my mother, I see her stress lines deepen. I know the answer is no before they even tell me. My father's bank account begins free-fall-ing into the negative, just from buying us Christmas presents. He grows accustomed to chipping away pieces of his bones to strengthen us. I've never once heard him complain.

***

I am twelve years old. My teachers tell me I'm so advanced; I get to be in a high school class. I tell my mother, and she cries. She tells me how proud she is that I built myself into this. When my father applauds after hearing my poetry, it sounds better than a full concert hall of adoring fans. My parents wish me a pedestal so I can reach all my biggest dreams. When they can't afford one, they instead craft one of true foundations. The brick is made up of different jobs, each recycled and re-used throughout the years. The mortar is in the form of re-minders, moments cemented in my brain stem that are strong enough for me to stand on.

***

I am seventeen years old. I am on the eve of greatness; I am every October 30th and December 24th rolled into one. I am too anxious to proceed. I stare at blank applications until the Social Security number fills itself in. I have never known a world where I was not less than or equal to. My future feels like an unfinished math equation. My tongue is molded from eraser shavings.

My mother is scared. She allows her fears to swallow her up from the inside, until she becomes a black hole, and now her gravity is dragging me down with her. She wields colliding asteroids with the will of her paranoia: deportation and loneliness. I am gripping onto G.P.A.s and S.A.T. scores with white knuckles and rotting hope. I feel my fingers decaying quicker than I can search for scholarships.

My father knocks on my door and sits on the edge of my bed.

"N.O.V.A. is a good school, *sabes*?" he looks at me for a moment, his eyes agreeing with my mother's preemptive lonely nest syndrome. I nod and meet his gaze with a thin-lipped smile.

"I'm applying," I tell him. I don't tell him that they don't offer financial aid to immigrants, or that we won't be able to afford it.

"*Que bueno.*"

# Embracing Frankenstein

**NICK JOHNSON**, Grade 12, Age 17. Prairie High School,
Cedar Rapids, IA. Lori Danker, *Educator*

"Life, although it may only be an accumulation of anguish, is
dear to me, and I will defend it."

—Mary Shelley, *Frankenstein*

As a disabled individual, albeit one who can halfway pass for
able-bodied, acknowledging all parts of my identity is very important to me. For me, my limp is often the thing people notice
first. Especially recently, as I've been growing, chronic pain
has become another day-to-day occurrence. Having had thirteen surgeries in my seventeen years, various parts of my body
—including my back, both shoulders, and both hips—are often
stiff and painful. Popping pills to manage my pain is nothing
new to me, but a couple of Tylenol a few times a day doesn't
always solve the problem. For the most part, I've conditioned
myself to grin and bear it, a sarcastic comment usually not far
behind.

Another effect of cerebral palsy that I deal with on a daily
basis is a heightened startle reflex. The sensitivity tends to
fluctuate from day to day. This manifests itself something like

this: Some days I don't flinch when someone drops a heavy box a foot away from me; others, I jump a mile when someone sneezes loudly from across the classroom. Responses range from societally rote apologies to mockery. What people don't realize or care about, however, is that

A. it's a reflex,

B. eighty-five percent of the time, they didn't legitimately scare me (see point A), and

C. while I generally react (read: startle) and move on, it's not that simple mentally; I am horribly self-conscious about it.

Part of me has always wanted to make a moment out of it and finally stand up to everyone and educate them (forcefully if necessary) about how this affects my life. However, I know this would just give those people who mock me the reaction they so desperately crave. I'm hoping college, with its "fresh start, reinventing yourself" approach, will give me a chance to educate my peers there before they can fixate on the startle in a negative light.

My other diagnosis is hydrocephalus, one that accounts for six of the thirteen surgeries I've had. While I haven't had to have brain surgery in eleven years and counting, it's the most nerve-racking of all my surgeries. For the most part, the doctors just have to adjust the valve in my head with a large magnet. However, there have been a few occasions where the entire system goes bad, and they have to replace it. That involves going in through my stomach to look at the tubing, and in my head to replace the main technical component. I've often considered the many reasons I could never be a brain surgeon, my jumpiness very high on that list. Because of all that, skilled surgeons are people I really appreciate.

For the past several years, I've wondered what life would be like if I didn't have a disability. Would I trade out the art that

I'm passionate about now for something else entirely? Would I take up football, provided I was able to bulk up my muscles? These and similar questions go through my head to some extent almost daily. While there's obviously no way to answer them, it's an interesting concept to ponder. Athletics are more likely than not off the list for college, but I'm interested to see where my interests (graphic design, writing, and photography) will take me in secondary education.

One grand misconception most people have about those with a physical disability is that a cognitive impairment goes hand in hand with it, when that is not always true. In my case, I am aged up by adults, yet treated generally as "other" by my peers. The latter accomplishes nothing except adding to what I've realized is a caustically bitter side of myself, one that comes out through my twisted sense of humor and self-deprecation.

This dark humor hasn't lent itself to much, outside of internalizing way too much and struggling to open up to people. Depression and anxiety have been a part of my life for my entire high school career, and both have led to some bleak moments. I've had to deal with friends cutting me out of their lives because I'm "overdramatic" and "self-centered" for trying to articulate the mess in my head. However, these struggles have allowed me to see who my real friends are—those who stand by me even when I'm at my lowest.

The physical aspects of having cerebral palsy—while a large part of my life—really just serve to foster the mental, emotional, and social components that make me me. From dealing with chronic pain to coping with my hyperactive startle reflex, from how to manage my CP societally to educating that very society on my diagnoses, I've learned many valuable lessons along the way. My aim in life is to teach others that yes, I'm different, but I am not other.

# Under the Shade of the Apple Tree

**MYRA KAMAL**, Grade 7, Age 13. Rancho Solano Preparatory School, Scottsdale, AZ. Ellon Sears, *Educator*

America? I always asked my parents why they chose to move to America. Why did they leave Pakistan? I would always get a watery answer in return. To gain the opportunity to earn money? To fulfill their American dreams? I didn't even think they knew the answer. I found when other strangers asked me why my parents did, I would lose the authority over the conversation. This question started to weigh more heavily on my mind a few years ago, when we invited our new neighbors over.

My father was always a gardener. Living in dry Phoenix, Arizona, motivated him to make our backyard mock an exotic Indonesian jungle surrounded by a sea of plain blue. I'd always watch him through the window. I was never a gardener. My father would start with nothing but a seed and its roots. I've always wondered how a luscious tree can originate from such a miniscule dot that can easily slip between my fingers. But then again, the world is a dot in the universe isn't it? I like to think a tree's roots are its origin. Over time, my father nursed the new plant, exposing it to the real world. He worked without gloves because he wanted to feel the earth. He felt the rich American soil in which he stood on as an immigrant, a citizen, and a father. However, he always stood on American soil as a Pakistani and as a Muslim. Throughout all the labels in his life, it all started with his roots. Nonetheless, there were thorns embedded in the soil that would strike his fingers, and his blood would pepper the ground. I watched as my father devoted days to take care of his plant over the years. He not only sacrificed a little of his blood, but his energy, time, and the warmth of the inside when the bitter frost would sweep in on cold winter days. The actual fruit of his labor showed when one warm summer, the tree bore plump, ripe, red apples. The red shade was as dark as my father's blood that spilt upon the tree's soil. It was beautiful. The apples shone like big red pearls in the sunshine. I remembered that would not be possible without a seed and its roots.

Our new neighbor's daughter visited us a few days later. The seven-year-old had hair as yellow as the sun and freckles sprinkled across her face. It was an enjoyable afternoon, full of swimming and laughter. My father even let her have a few of the apples on the tree. Then her parents came to pick her up in the evening. While the parents made small talk, suddenly Adhan started going off in the house, the sound echoing across the walls. Adhan is the Islamic call to prayer. It probably sounded like a string of gibberish to our neighbors. On the contrary, they recognized the sound. I caught a hint of fear and distaste in their eyes. Furthermore, they tightened their grip on their daughter.

"We didn't know you were Muslim," the mom explained to my mother. The tension in the air was thick and choppy.

"Yes, we are," replied my mother with her head held high. Our new neighbors then left in a hurry without another word.

The next morning we received a letter of complaint from our neighborhood association. Our new neighbors had complained to them last night, that apparently my father's apple tree was an eyesore to spectate from their window because he had planted it too close to the fence. I was really disappointed because I thought our families were friends. My family and I knew they made this preposterous and trivial complaint about the apple tree because we were Muslims. Because we were different, we were looked down upon and scrutinized for it. However, the sad thing was that I automatically knew the reason for my neighbors' actions. When did my innocence leave me? Nonetheless, even though I knew all of this, I never understood it. Wasn't this supposed to be the country of freedom and diversity? Whatever happened to the immigrant's American Dream? Wasn't America the Melting Pot? It seems like the Melting Pot is just a vision America is still trying to attain. This country is diverse, but without the tolerance for it, none of that matters. I realized that there is a price for all immigrants if given the chance to walk on American soil. People would try to turn their identity into a burden weighing heavily on their back.

That was when the question dawned on me. Why did my parents want to move to America, when they most likely knew they would not be completely welcome? Why did my parents sacrifice so much just to endure the hate that they were rewarded with? I was lying down under the shade of the apple tree looking up at the sky when I was thinking about this. The grass was cool and ticklish on my face as I gazed up at the vast blue. I could have been looking at this sky from Pakistan and it would have been the same sky. I would not have the shade of this apple tree though. Later in the day, I approached my father in the garden. He was tending to the tulips he had just planted.

"You are not going to get the tree cut down because of their complaint, right?" I asked my father hopefully.

"Of course not. I've worked hard on the tree and will not let that be wasted by something as evanescent as this. Something so beautiful cannot be touched by such neglect. It is not worth it," he assured me.

My father walked across the yard and plucked a red pearl off the tree and offered it to me. I bit into the crisp apple and let the warm, sweet juice dribble down my chin like golden honey. Tasting that juicy apple answered the question I had always wondered about. Why did my parents move to America? They sacrificed everything to move to America so that my sister and I could have the best opportunities despite the lack of welcome. My dad worked hard so that we could enjoy the fruit of his work. He grew a life around him just so that beautiful opportunities were only a pluck out of reach for us. I could see many glistening red opportunities over my head. I am still in awe whenever I think that it all started with nothing but my father and his roots. America? My father moved to America so that I could enjoy the rich apples off of his tree.

# My Cousin Ethan

**MAXWELL SURPRENANT**, Grade 8, Age 14. St. Sebastian's School, Needham, MA. David Cornish, *Educator*

The person I admire most is my cousin Carmelito Ethan Olaes. His initials spell CEO. When Ethan was born, his parents had big dreams for him—he would have a lot of friends, he would play music and sports, he would go to college, and maybe someday he would run his own company. Those dreams deflated when at nearly two years old, he received the diagnosis: autism. Ethan couldn't talk. He had sensory issues. He walked on his tiptoes, and he flapped his arms. But I've got the best spoiler alert for you: He learned to fly.

Blessed with a supportive and loving family, Ethan received early intervention and made progress. He learned to talk and walk even if he developed at a slower rate. He still has trouble looking people in the eye and holding a conversation, but he keeps working at it. Through it all, here's what we discovered: Ethan is a savant, which means he's a genius.

My grandmother has a jukebox with hundreds of entries, and Ethan can name every song and its corresponding number. After we watch a movie, Ethan often recites all the credits. We never get lost when we are with Ethan because he memorizes the map in minutes. When we went on a family vacation to Disneyworld, Ethan led the way around the park. He loves roller coasters. He puts his hands up in the air and smiles ear to ear.

A musical prodigy, Ethan has perfect pitch. He's skillful with more than eight instruments, but piano is his forte. He can play the work of the greatest composers and the best rock bands by sight reading or simply listening. At twelve years old, he began studying at the prestigious Oberlin Music Conservatory. At sixteen, he made his debut at Carnegie Hall. Recently, he was honored as Kawai's First Young Artist, and he'll tour around the world.

Ethan has found a way to connect with people through his beautiful music. It flows like a river. He is the heart and inspiration of his family's nonprofit, called ETHAN, which stands for Everyone Together Help Autism Now. His own company is called Ethan88—88 keys on the keyboard. His tagline is: "Let music move us." Ethan plays the piano at various charity events to raise awareness and funds for important causes.

In October, my parents and I traveled to Cleveland to watch Ethan perform at the Alleluia Ball at the Huntington Convention Center. The event raised over $1 million for the "Better Together" initiative, an inclusive program adopted by 46 Catholic schools in northeast Ohio. It provides children with special needs the opportunity to receive and benefit from a Catholic education. This diversity not only benefits the ones with learning challenges, but also lifts up all the students, teachers, faculty, and community at large. It brings out the best in everyone, as we are at our finest when we are compassionate and giving. The greatest lesson we can learn is empathy, the ability to put oneself in someone else's shoes. We must remember that we are each other's keepers.

After Ethan's flawless performance, he received a standing ovation. Like most everyone in the room, I felt an overwhelming sense of admiration, gratitude, and joy. Ethan has worked hard and overcome obstacles bigger than mountains. Many people put limitations on him; but fortunately, Ethan is surrounded by people who believe in him—his parents, family, friends, teachers, and kind strangers. It's a shame that some people look at Ethan and turn away; they are uncomfortable around people who are different. Ethan's standing ovation was a triumph because everyone looked past Ethan's disability and saw his ability.

What about sports? Ethan can run a mile in five minutes and jump rope 250 revolutions in a minute and 26 seconds exactly. On family bike rides, he can pedal the fastest. He races ahead, and then waits patiently for all of us to catch up. Ethan can pocket 15 pool balls in a row. I'll never beat him in chess or cards. I joke that someday I'll take him to the casinos with me. He doesn't get the joke, but that's okay. Nobody is perfect.

Now, where did you place your bet? Against the odds, Carmelito Ethan Olaes is coming out ahead of the game. It's not easy, but this seventeen-year-old CEO is showing autism who's boss.

# Citric

**ALEXIS DEPINHO**, Grade 10, Age 16. St. John's School, Houston, TX.
Clay Guinn and Rachel Weissenstein, *Educators*

you tasted like blood oranges, like ascorbic acid stinging
in those liminal spaces where fingertip meets nail.

this is how the peel unravels:
like ribbons on imaginary presents; imaginary like
my thinning blood and your happiness and kissing you
felt like pulling apart those twelve morsels of time,
prying each second from the hands of the clock and
sinking my poison-brittle teeth into the hours
i spent hating myself
for wanting you.

darling, you are a timepiece,
always watching, always waiting,
the tick-tick-ticking behind your eyes
an unsteady rhythm, like a half-lit candle
flickering softly under your breath,
or the careful sound of glass
as she breaks & breaks,
or the slow drip of juice
down my chin as i
clock out

# Instructions for Building a Nation

**AMMA OTCHERE**, Grade 11, Age 16. Menomonee Falls High School, Menomonee Falls, WI. Beth Larson, *Educator*

Kidnap a people from their homeland. Stack them on a ship until all you see is flesh, bodies blurred into an obsidian sea. Stumble through the dark and dank with your hand over your nose as you prod the limbs littered around you, checking for the soft give of decay. Lead the ones that survive, dirt from the West African earth still caked under their fingernails, to a foreign land.
Call it resettlement.

Rob a people of their culture, of their identity. Teach these people that the white man is king. Tell them to hate their skin. Force them to forget that they come from warriors and kings, from merchants and sailors, from places with names and families with pride. Try to convince them that they are nobody at all.
Call it reeducation.

Spit in the face of the man stripped naked on the auction block. Call him Robert, call him Paul, call him Timothy. When you see his refusal to respond in the set of his jaw, Call him retarded.

Watch a man desperately fight to preserve his humanity. Dangle it over his head. Let him get close enough that he can

smell its aroma. Taste its implications on his tongue. When it no longer draws laughter from your lips, stamp him down to preserve the joke.
Call it a rebellion.

Whip a man until a stream of red courses beneath him. Tear away his skin like you are stripping a leather hide. Hoist this man on a rope by his raw neck. Let his children watch him suffer.
Call it a reminder.

Sell a woman's child when you're low on money. Watch her spirit deflate as she pleads, eyes wild with hopelessness, deep and endless. Sell her children one by one, until she weeps as soon as her baby is born, holding him to her chest without ever looking him in the eye.
Call it refinancing.

Go to church every Sunday. Take your hat off in the chapel archway. Ask Jesus to forgive your
sins. Use that same mouth to tell that nigger boy to get your carriage ready.
Call it redemption.

Emancipate a man, then force him to work off the debt he still owes you. Don't tell him that blood debts can never be repaid, that his ancestors cry out from under your floor-boards every night, so loud that your ears ring whenever you close your eyes. Watch him toil for a freedom he will never know by name.
Call it release.

Allow a man to farm your land for a share of the crop. Never allow a penny to touch his calloused fingers. Call it sharecropping with a wink and a smirk at your friends turned accomplices.
Don't call it re-enslavement.

Watch a man rise to empower his people. Observe as hope fills their faces until they, too, have a dream. Spy on this man. Degrade this man. Threaten this man. When you finally kill this man,
Call him a reprobate.

Choke a man until he can no longer tell you that he can't breathe. Don't question the justice of a death sentence for selling loose cigarettes: You understand and the jury understands that this is not about the dead man, toe to toe with his ancestors under New York cement. This is about averted eyes, and sotto voce remarks, and a misplaced fear so strong that it fills the courtroom with its stench. Recoil at its acrid smell when you hear the jury
Call it rectified.

Talk about this history in words that criss-cross like mismatched whip marks on a smooth expanse of skin. Trip over the traps you create, fill the gaps in your speech with clay fortified by black gold, pretend not to see its shine. Tiptoe around your words, as if the destruction of bodies can be described with anything but brute force. Teach this delicate, evasive art to the students in your schools, let history fade into shadow and smoke.
Call it rewritten.

# Nothing but the Truth

**CHARLIE HASTINGS**, Grade 9, Age 14. Charleston County School of the Arts, North Charleston, SC. Danielle DeTiberus, Francis Hammes, and Elizabeth Hart, *Educators*

The poem sits
On the defendant's chair
As dazed as the fraternity kids in the morning.
The poem's cheeks shine red as roses,
Eyes like stars, clichés openly seep from his body
Like pus from a pimple.

A certain pair of glaring eyes sits to the poem's left
In the plaintiff's chair, a hater of clichés, Congress, and his
mother. Obviously
Scared only of his morning yogurt.
The plaintiff was a contemporary man
He wore glasses marketed as only the best for spying inner
meaning
With a pen tucked away in his front pocket, epitomized for
spurting only
The most poetic of lines.

All rise, said the judge
Nobody stood, except for the plaintiff

The judge seated everyone in a passive tone,
The plaintiff was last to sit.
He dispensed with the pleasantries, making sure the poem
Swore on his best line

That he would tell nothing but the truth.
He explained the charges, use of cliché and dishonesty, off-
tone language, nonsensicalness, and lack of proper
Lineation, grammar, and sophisticated language.

How does he plead?
Guilty only of the last six, the poem said,
Things switched over to the prosecutor.

The poem, he started
Had irregular lineation, the grammar usage was putrid at
best, and language unsound.
Similar, he said, to the pages occupied by the tile courtroom
floors
And the lines of a poem who couldn't stand up. Yet I cannot
figure
What the poem means, it's nonsensicalness clouds me.
Might be about the profundity of sunsets, or the sky, or stars!
Perhaps it was about the liveliness that came with long walks
on the beach,
Missing car keys, or staph!

I think line 21 was telling us something, said the attorney,
perhaps about
The pure rawness of poetry? The honesty?
It certainly explains the setting, the title as well.

Or perhaps lines 5 through 6, said the jury, it certainly
portrayed
How we must look inside ourselves
For what poetry really means!

Cliché! Cliché! said the prosecutor, it would not be fit
For something as grand as poetry!
This poem even, in itself
Has no meaning, no flair, no pop
It is like soda left out on a hot summer day!
And what the hell is wrong with
the breaks anyway, free verse?
It's as if a millennial wrote this poem!

Unresponsiveness from the jury, naturally consisting
Of poems that spoke of a lover's eyes
As the stars and a universe where the people worship
The night. The nostalgia behind the peppermints
On a grandmother's mantel.

The stand was an
Ironic name to the poem, since
Of course he could not stand
At the stand, only testify meaning
In his bleak lines, what did he mean?
Was it a sin to be nothing? No
The prosecutor
Couldn't have thought so.

# Fur Trading

**CHRISTOPHER BARLOW**, Grade 10, Age 15. South Portland High School, South Portland, ME. Tasha Graff, *Educator*

we were two dead swans waiting to be stuffed full of love and displayed to the world.

we ran like kids through the trees because that's all we were. out of fear, out of shame, your lips never touched my skin again.

hidden together in the hollowed oak hoping they find a doe to fill full of buckshot instead.
watch my skin recoil at every pull of a trigger.

welcome to the forest of hidden secrets and buried closet keys, green-eyed boys hide in the dark with shovels. green-eyed boys turn my heart to stone.

cup your hands downstream to drink some more, cup your hands around my face to christen this love. don't let them get to you, don't let yourself think you need to leave this to be holy.

in a log cabin in eau clare, wisconsin, you hold the rosary to my neck and i the razor to your wrist. i will break first, and you know this. i will write about your hands and your scars, and you will feed off of it.

you hate me, i can see it in your eyes. you hate yourself too,
i can feel it in the stars you choose to stare at and the verses
you know by heart.

drape the fur across your back and pretend that you are the
one in control. dig your fangs into a real man until you taste
sincerity.

    is the confessional honest? how many seconds does it take
for the words to spill into your lap?

    can you hear it?
   the sound of the wild?
you will be among them soon, those who seek souls expend-
able,

    only to end up buried under the ivy.

**RACHEL LEVINE**, *Fracture*, Photography. Grade 12, Age 17, Dixie Hollins High School, Kenneth City, FL. Kristen Pineda, *Educator*

# Where I'm From

**CRYSTAL CENTENO-PADILLA**, Grade 12, Age 17. South High School,
Denver, CO. Nicholas Shelke, *Educator*

I am from framed Virgen de Guadalupe photos on the wall,
From tamales and dulce de leche.
I am from a small home.
Where the smell of Fabuloso fills the rooms.
I am from home-grown peppers,
That get tossed into every dish.
My carved name,
on the quaking aspen bark in my front yard.

I am from piñata birthday parties and intercambios
navideños.
From Centeno and Padilla.
From motorcycle rides and green eyes.

I'm from "Angel de mi guarda, de mi dulce compañía"
And "No me desampares, ni de noche, ni de día."
I'm from "Bidi Bidi Bon Bon" by Selena Quintanilla,
I'm from spicy and feisty.

I'm from Jalisco,
From missing thumbs
And spilling caldo de camaron.

I'm from dancing horses
and Quinceañera dresses.
From dirt roads.

From agua de rosa soaked skin
That glows.

I'm from "Corelle!"
And "Espérate!"
It's never enough time.
Necesitaba más tiempo contigo.
Pero nunca será demasiado tiempo.

I'm from "Speak English, you're in America."
And from "Cállate pinche gringo."

I am from te quiero
And te amo.
Not from I love you.

# My Mother's Favorite Drugstore Wine

**KATE GRAYSON**, Grade 12, Age 18. Charleston County School of the Arts, North Charleston, SC. Danielle DeTiberus, Francis Hammes, and Elizabeth Hart, *Educators*

My mother drinks wine from the drugstore
down the corner in a Waterford crystal glass.
It is always sauvignon blanc, and she holds it
in her mouth for a moment before she swallows
it so that she can taste it for a minute longer.
The wine is light and the color of honey and
her hair and she sits on the back porch with
her legs crossed, looking at the grass and
thinking of how maybe she should cut it soon
or maybe plant some flowers near the gate.
She likes flowers, but can never keep them alive.

# My Voice, a Burden to You

**MADDY BARKER**, Grade 9, Age 14. Miami Arts Charter School, Miami, FL. Jen Karetnick and Ariel Lewis, *Educators*

I'd been restrained
by many hands my whole life
but they were barely enough
to keep my mouth shut.
My tongue, my teeth, and my words
only got me into trouble.

I couldn't control the things I said.

If you tried to hold your palm over my mouth,
your fingers would disintegrate.
My opinions still being shooed away
by your cracked fingertips.

This voice burned in your ears like acid,
obnoxiously barking at your words
and forever being the annoyance in your brains.

You could rip the teeth out of my gums,
nail my lips shut with a hammer
and pray that you wouldn't hear me speak,

although it'd never be enough to keep me quiet,
even for just a minute.

# Blk Girl Depression

**NAHISHA JACKSON**, Grade 11, Age 16. East Lyme High School,
East Lyme, CT. Rick Clark, *Educator*

Blk girls can't be depressed
depression has reserved a parking spot marked
for spoiled white girls
Dying for pity is their hobby

depression is for those who haven't struggled
whose greatest hardship is deciding between millennial or
baby pink lipstick
Blk girls don't fit the requirements
Blk girls are too busy dodging bullets aimed at their
womanhood and skin
Blk girls can't be depressed

depression has declared
you can't sit with us
only seats are reserved for angsty white girls who thrift for fun
not the hood blk girls who do it out of necessity

depression is for the Sharon's and Ashley's
not the Destiny's and Ayesha's,
Blk girls are too worried about being othered
too busy defending
nurturing
keeping alive our kind
too busy being ignored
Blk womanhood to dust
flowers of red blooming from our crowns of 4c

leaving behind our sweet, soft voices
not only for others but for ourselves
We rise
from the ground to become guardians over ourselves

Blk girls can't be depressed
red drops scattered on pale skin
never brown
thick like honey, our blood drips from arms with purpose
purpose: to be

when Blk girl is depressed
she becomes the strangled roots of a community
ripped from herself
tossed into the torment of our identities

no chance for goodbyes
farewells
exchanged phone numbers
ripped.
plucked before harvest

Blk girls too hurt
our hurt is unique
cannot be fathomed
cannot be compared
our hurt is a web of the burdens of our resistance
and blood family

Blk girls can be depressed
Blk girls nurture themselves
no one else will

Milk we feed is spit out
desire turned to blond heads wearing our faces
When Blk girls are depressed

**KALLAN PAULSEN**, *Sentinel*, Drawing & Illustration. Grade 12, Age 17, Bondurant-Farrar High School, Bondurant, IA.
Christian Vandehaar, *Educator*

# After Harvey

**RUKMINI KALAMANGALAM**, Grade 12, Age 16. Carnegie Vanguard High School, Houston, TX. Rachel Bohenick, *Educator*

The first rain after the hurricane
We held our breath
Imagined what it would feel like to be drowning again
So soon after the taste of stolen air
Replaced the salty breathlessness of rising tides

The first rain after the hurricane
We were ready before the flash-flood warning, already watching as
Water lapped at the curb,
Feasted on the rotted remains of gutted houses,
Tried to wash away the evidence of its crimes

The first rain after the hurricane,
We saw a pack of wild dogs at CVS
Snarling and slavering in red wellington boots
They watched us with hungry eyes,
Snouts sniffing the air for threats from the sky & each other

The first rain after the hurricane,
The water washed away as quick as it had come
Leaving streets dark & empty &
Water still priced 3.99 a gallon
We scoured the clouds for signs of false promises

# Untitled

**AKILAH TONEY**, Grade 10, Age 15. New Orleans Center for Creative Arts, New Orleans, LA. Lara Naughton, *Educator*

i hate my black black skin
i hate my nappy nappy hair
i hate my big big lips
i hate my broad broad nose

i can't play in the sun too long
cause i might get blacker

would he like me if i was Light skin
loose Bouncy Curls and a Thin nose
mama put two creamy Relaxers in my hair
i don't want no nigga afros
what if i was Skinnier
what if my thighs were Thinner
everybody at recess says
they like the Blonde Barbie dolls
better than the darker ones like mine
they like the cotton-candy Blue eyes
and Silky golden bone Straight hair
a pink skirt, a matching purse, and skin real Fair

my cousins say I'm fat and black ugly
i say no i'm not
they say yes you is
i say no i'm not
they say yes you is

# Sky People

**SALIHAH AAKIL**, Grade 9, Age 14. Home School, Silver Spring, MD.
Latifa Barnett, *Educator*

The sky is blue, but at nighttime it's black. There are no blue
people, which is to say that black folks are the nearest things
to skybound, closest in kin to universes, first and last
children of the spinning expanse.

We are starborn and soaring, surviving on the streets,
reminding ourselves that there's always a night sky to return
to. Reminding ourselves that we can take shelter in the dark,
because blackness is the only thing that loves blackness.

We hide from sirens here, where fear can't fly high enough
to hurt us. We shine here and laugh when they mistake our
bright eyes for constellations.

We were the first people to reach the sky. Ended as fragments
of heaven walking on Earth, star moon and sun personified.
Each one of us a galaxy, features forming planets, eyes and
smiles shining like stars, our throats forming black holes with
words worthy of getting lost in.

And when we die, our souls follow a star path straight to
heaven.

# Body Writings

**WILLIAM LOHIER**, Grade 11, Age 16. Stuyvesant High School, New York, NY. Maura Dwyer, *Educator*

you draw into your arm.
Etched-into skin
Seeking human
Underneath.
you remember experiments done on your Body.
Trapped in a sleep
Deprivation chamber.
Suspended
In a place
out beyond ideas
Of right-doing and wrong-doing
There was your body,
A field.
you remember being planted in.
you remember looking over the operating table,
Reading the Manual:

"Handle the Boy's body with caution.
First, remove the face.
Then the tongue.
Then the rage."

you stripped.
Unzipped your skin, sweating.
Slowly you removed your face so he didn't have to.
One by one you plucked out your teeth so you could no longer
smile.

One by one you removed your eyes so you could no longer be
seen.
You cannot hang a face.
Empty eyes cannot kick at air.
Airless nostrils cannot long for the earth.

After,
your body,
Stripped of its rage,
Fell to the ground.
Was swallowed up and became a field.
Was born again as a tree
Round which they tied a noose.
As they dragged more boys to be lynched,
You did your best to cool them with your shade
As their feet lifted off the ground.
flying.

# When Black Kids Time Travel, They Don't—

**ZAIN-MINKAH MURDOCK**, Grade 12, Age 17. North Mecklenburg High
School, Huntersville, NC. Amanda Soesbee, *Educator*

I wanna press my palm against Claudette Colvin's stomach
And feel life shift behind her ribs,
Feel the movement quake
and rumble
and begin—

I wanna steady the shoulder of Rosa Parks
As the bus sways to a stop,
Adjust my knees so she can step off
First—the driver says,
Have a good day, miss
Waves the folding doors closed
As she walks on
And keeps on walking—

I wanna wind King's wire 'round my fingers,
Shut my eyes and let his sermons
lull me all the way
to that dream he was going on about,
Erase the tapes,
Coretta loves you, Coretta loves you,
Coretta loves you—

I wanna carry Ruby Bridge's books down the hallway
Catch the stares with my right fist and
Let them fall, hard,
onto the linoleum floor,
Whisper, "They're only looking at you
'cause you're so beautiful,"
So, so beautiful—

I wanna slide a quarter 'cross the counter for Emmett Till
Maybe for some Mary Janes or Tootsie Rolls
Or Bazooka Gum,
Maybe he'll beam, puff out his cheeks;
   blow, and scrape the pink residue
from his lips with his teeth—

I wanna sip chocolate milkshakes with John Lewis,
Swing my legs from a silver stool,
Make small talk about the slushy Nashville snow,
He'll echo,
Are you cold?
And, with a charming flourish,
maybe offer me his coat—

I wanna read Marx and Lenin with Angela Davis
Every few moments a page will flip too fast,
Liberation, she'll resound
And the sky will become a graveyard
For the lumpenproletariat
And my head will nod in understanding—

I wanna watch the wind roar as Ali throws
one, two, three punches—

Lunge, jump, leap, shut the door,
don't let the draft in—

I wanna Lindy Hop in the Audubon with Malcolm X
See if his smile is more of the sun
than the photographs say
Maybe he'll slip his horned browlines atop my nose
Grin, As-Salaam-Alaikum
And his warbling voice will carry
What silver bullets cannot—

I wanna lay in wet grass with Gordon Parks,
In overalls and white tennis shoes,
He'll turn to me and say,
Camera whirring, June bug stringing,
Yes, this is my shot—

I wanna offer my right earbud to James Baldwin,
watch his lips curl as Stubbs croons,
I can't help myself,
And Baldwin's fingers will do a little tap-dance
And his pen will waltz across the paper
And—maybe he'll write
About me, yes—
Maybe he will write about me.

# Bulletproof Scarf

**AKHIYAR ABDI**, Grade 10, Age 15. School of the Arts, Rochester, NY.
Marcy Gamzon, *Educator*

My mother had finally let me
into the store alone.
I felt like a grown-up with her credit card clenched tightly
beneath my fingers.
I helped the clerk load the items into the cart.
Eggs,
Milk,
Bread.
I felt so grown up.

"Hurry up, dirty terrorist."

The words came out fast and rapid
as if shot out of the barrel of a gun.
I turned around and froze in my spot,
staring at my shooter.

My father always says
Let the words go into one ear
and come back
out of the other.

I wanted to listen, but once these words
entered my ear
they began to
circle my brain,

repeating that motion as they tightened
and tightened,
and tightened,
squeezing all of my thoughts dry.

The cotton material of my hijab
suddenly felt soft, absorbing
the hatred that exuded
from him.

Had the bullet gone any farther
it would have pierced my skull,
flying past the armor
and lying still in between the hollow.

I had nothing to fear
because the tag on my scarf read bulletproof.
And because I had learned to face away
and expel the ammunition.

And because when the bullet hit my scarf
it left a single dent in my hijab
before it fell away, clinking against the floor,
pressed from my armor.

# Deconstruction

**DANELLE ANTELO**, Grade 12, Age 17. Miami Arts Charter School, Miami, FL. Jen Karetnick and Ariel Lewis, *Educators*

Your father worked in construction,
so I assumed he would have taught
you how to lay down a strong foundation.

I've never had the pleasure to
meet the man he raised;
instead I live with the hollow remain
of a building that was never finished.

You take the form of your most recent
lover and undergo a metamorphosis.
You've never had to stand on a base
of your own making.

You sit on the curb of mediocrity
and I can't help but wonder where
my father went. If I see him again
I'll make sure to ask.

# Labor of Love

**BRINDA RAO**, Grade 12, Age 17. Edgemont Jr. Senior High School, Scarsdale, NY. Angela Dixcy, *Educator*

Your first memory of Ammamma is red.

The itchy material of her sari against your soft, young cheeks. Red like the bindi she presses into your brow. She kisses the bridge of your nose with cracked lips.

"Gunde," she cries in Telugu. Her voice is music—a tempo of curled vowels and starched consonants. "My heart."

She hugs you to her body, folding your innocence in the scent of mothballs and what you imagine the sun smells like.

You wear the bindi for an hour before scratching it off in annoyance.

\*\*\*

It's your first Indian Diwali. Your papa does not know the rules for little girls. He does not know how to slip your gangly limbs into the shalwar kameez in your closet. It had been months since you'd worn it. By the time Ammamma finds it, there's a layer of dust across the bejeweled front.

She rubs her thumb along the hole at the bottom of the skirt with a frown.

You wake on Diwali to the green dress splayed out on your bed. Ammamma helps you dress, teaching you how to use safety pins to keep the shalwar kameez in place.

"Did you teach my amma too?"

She is silent. The words that break from your teeth are hollow, carefree to you. You feel her hand squeeze your shoulder as she inhales deeply. At last, she places a ruby bindi on your forehead.

That night you light your first Diwali lantern. Ammamma holds your hands in hers as she teaches you how to make kolams.

It rains through the late hours. The colorful sand butterfly you made drips down the stairs the next morning.

*** 

If you are good, she plucks all the seeds from a pomegranate for you. Papa chastises her for overworking her hands, but Ammamma grins and watches you eat.

Your papa calls it a labor of love, to work through the chambers of the fruit. To pluck the gemstone arils free so meticulously. To sing the songs of Andra Pradesh that you cannot know in your bones like she does. She works the pomegranates like a harp, making music of albedo.

You go to school with purple-stained fingers.

You kiss Ammamma's cheeks before running wild.

Pomegranate seeds slush around your insides, making the day into an ocean.

*** 

When you are seven, she plaits your hair in the morning. In and out. Ammamma's hands shake but she holds your locks calmly. Telugu fills the silence between the two of you as she whispers of the stories from Moparru.

You imagine the green fields of rice where she grew up.

You imagine the thatched homes and the dusty ground.

When Ammamma finishes her stories of home, she undoes the plait and starts again. You are silent, listening to her hum the songs she once sang to your amma. You are silent, listening to the tears she sheds for your amma.

\*\*\*

You are nine and speak to Ammamma once a month on the phone. Ammamma is in Moparru, braiding another girl's hair. You see the photos on your papa's laptop, staring at them in confusion. She is your ammamma—you do not like to share.

"Come to New York," you beg her. You hear silence on her end of the phone and begin to bawl. "Ammamma, I miss you."

She finally ignores your request, telling you about the new dog your grandfather bought for their farm.

\*\*\*

You begin to forget the Telugu that Ammamma fed you. You lose the vibrancy of words, turning to English for comfort. When friends ask about your amma, you tell them that your mom is dead. When Ammamma calls, you answer her in English. You're dancing a waltz to her tango. It breaks her heart, you imagine years later, that you are losing India.

You stare at the books she read to you years ago and cannot recognize the letters.

Telugu looks like art on paper, inked cranes dancing across worn pages. You shut those books and put them deep inside your closet.

\*\*\*

It hits you when you are twelve that Ammamma is not coming back. There will be no more pomegranate feasts. Your hair will fly wild in the wind as you sprint across your backyard.

"I don't want to speak to Ammamma anymore," you complain to your papa. He frowns and puts you on the phone with her.

She questions away, switching from Telugu to English when you do not answer.

"Gunde?"

You are stone.

***

You are fourteen, staring at the house your papa grew up in. Roses and vines trail over the sides, and you can hear Shakespeare breathing between the rooms. There are no bowls of pomegranate seeds in your grandmum's house, but she keeps a tin of caramel candy for you.

You gorge on the sticky sweets during the long summer days. Your lips become stuck, and you feel India clipping away from your spine.

Grandmum hates your long hair; you wonder why you let it grow down to kiss the knot at your spine. Ammamma is not there to plait it. You let Grandmum take you to her hair salon and watch as the black curls fall to the ground.

"She has so much hair," the hairdresser exclaims. Your grandmum chuckles from behind her book.

"Gets it from her mother—Indian woman with the frizziest hair you could imagine!"

When your hair is short, you grasp the ends and feel ghosts clamoring for hugs.

***

You remember Ammamma crying when people called you Brenda. She loved your name, twisted it in her mouth and gargled up the letters with minty teeth.

"Brunda," she murmured against your hair. You disentangled your body from hers and teasingly say that Brunda was not your name.

You are sixteen and find that old shalwar kameez in your closet. You do not know who you are.

Papa takes you to Moparru when you are seventeen. The road is dirt and dust. The air is thick against your throat. It rattles into your lungs like a beast.

Insects hum from the great palm trees that stretch over the sea of rice fields. You close your eyes and feel the monsters lurking in the tills. The car you ride in burps up complaint as it struggles through the countryside.

You no longer imagine the rice fields and thatched roofs.

The stories of your childhood come to life before your eyes.

There are holes in the roofs and mud in the fields. The sky is cloudy, moist with humidity. It feels like music, like the hum of the songs you'd almost forgotten.

Ammamma is waiting for you. She stands by the door of her cottage in a red-and-gold sari. You barely recognize her small frame. In your memories, she towered over you.

Now, she stares at you. Her eyes search your body first, then take to your face, scrubbing over it like she can wash away the years and make you into the motherless five-year-old she once knew.

Before you can speak, she moves forward and you are home. She presses you into her sari, the material scratching your arms. Your cheeks are high above her head, safe from the itchy material. You inhale her scent and grin, washed away in nostalgia.

"Gunde," she murmurs, holding you close. Her voice is glass, matching her shaking hands and her rattling cough. Her labors of love stain her hands. She was strong those years ago, holding your broken self to her. Now you take her and wrap your arms around her.

"Ammamma," you cry, letting tears for this, for India, flow free.

**ELENA GRANT**, *Self-Portrait in Gold*, Painting. Grade 12, Age 17, Plant Senior High School, Tampa, FL. Stacy Rosende, *Educator*

# At the Tone

**ISABELLA ERAULA**, Grade 10, Age 15. Goose Creek High School, Goose Creek, SC. Nicholas Geary, *Educator*

Voicemail from: Mom
2/17/15 0:17
Why aren't you home yet? I just woke up from waiting for you for so long and your father is . . . rampaging around the house right now. (rustling, followed by distant yelling) Get home.

Voicemail from: Penny
2/18/15 0:22
Hey, Gwen. I know you're probably in trouble right now. I just wanna say I'm sorry. You just looked so peaceful, and I know you're like, really tired, so I just left you alone. And you're a really heavy sleeper. I tried to wake you up on the third call, but you wouldn't budge. Your dad sounded really mad. I'm so sorry about all this. See you at school, I hope. Uhh, bye.

Voicemail from: Northville High School
2/24/15 0:25
Good evening, students and parents. Students taking the SAT and ACT are recommended to take tutoring courses after school during the week and this Saturday at 2 p.m. If you'd

like to schedule a session, speak with a teacher or one of our
guidance counselors. For more information, go to the school
website or give back a call. Thank you, and have a great day.

Voicemail from: Dad
3/8/15  0:09
Hello? Are you there? I'm right here. I'm right here. Nice. I'd
like a double cheese—(vomiting)

Voicemail from: Dad
3/8/15  0:42
(loud crackling noises) Take the chicken. Take the chicken.
It fell out of the freezer, you asshole. (pause) The dog! Ernie wants the chicken. He's trying to get the chicken. (glass
breaking) The chicken!!

Voicemail from: Dad
3/16/15 0:30
You piece of shit, where the hell are you? Off prancing around
again? I didn't ruin my life for you to be a worthless—(distant
yelling) What? I will say whatever I want to her face— No,
I'm not drunk! Shut up!! (yelling gets closer)

Voicemail from: Mom
4/18/15 0:08
Good morning, little Gwen, just reminding you that I love
you. Keep your head up and do good in school. You can make
it through today.

Voicemail from: Mom
5/5/15  0:05
Hi honey, could you go to the drugstore and pick me up some
medicine on your way home?

Voicemail from: Dad
5/5/15  0:16
I've decided that since you don't want to tell me where you
are and what you're doing, I'm going to take away your social
privileges. As soon as you get home, kiss your phone and
computer goodbye. If you deserve it, maybe you'll get them
back someday.

Voicemail from: Penny
6/12/15 0:12
Hey. I keep forgetting you got your phone taken away. Oops.
You might get annoyed when you finally get it back. I think
I'm just gonna leave you random messages in here. Bye!

Voicemail from: Unknown Number
6/23/15 0:12
Hey Katie, this is Dan. You left your scarf in my apartment
last night. I was wondering if you wanted it back or anything.
So just, call me back or whatever.

Voicemail from: Unknown Number
7/17/15 0:14
Is this Katie's number? Um, it's me, Dan. I don't know if you
remember me or not, but I still have your scarf. Come get it
back anytime, you know where I am.

Voicemail from: Unknown Number
8/9/15  0:11
Hey, it's Dan again. I'm starting to think that maybe you gave
me the wrong number. Hah, that's crazy, right? I'll keep tex-
ting just in case. Uhh, yeah. That's about it.

Voicemail from: Dad
9/24/15 0:12
Hi pumpkin, how's college treating ya? You better be studying hard. Ernie misses you, he's been clawing at your door every day. He's been a good boy. I'll send pictures of him. Take care, pumpkin, love you.

Voicemail from: Mom
10/17/15 0:25
Hey sweetie, I hope you have a safe flight. Come back home soon, and I'll make you your favorite five-cheese macaroni. I might need a little help too. My bones are getting a little frail, you know. If you can't come down here, we might visit you instead. Wouldn't that be fun? Well, I don't want to fill your inbox, so I'll be shutting up now. I love you, don't forget to take your meds.

Voicemail from: Penny
11/5/15 0:11
I'm really worried about you, please call back as soon as possible. I heard what happened. You know I'm right here, please reach out. I love you, alright?

Voicemail from: Jeffrey M.
11/5/15 0:15
Hey, I heard what happened with your mom. I'm so sorry. I'm always here if you need a shoulder to cry on. Everyone else is here too. Again, I'm so sorry for your loss.

Voicemail from: Penny
11/5/15 0:06
You haven't been answering any of my calls. I'm just going to come pick you up, okay?

Voicemail from: Christine R.

11/7/15  0:08

Yo, this is Christine from work. Heard about your situation, and I'm so sorry. I wish I could do something about it, but all I can do is be here. It'll get better, man.

Voicemail from: Unknown Number

6/9/16  0:21

Hello, is this Gwendolyn? It's Dad. Yeah, it's me. I am so sorry. I'm apologizing to you. To your mom. I acted poorly and didn't think for the most part. I've changed, if you would just meet me you would see. Just please talk to me.

Voicemail from: Unknown Number

7/14/16 0:34

It's Dad again. That number stopped sending you my calls, did you block my number again? Please, Gwendolyn. I've been sober for nine months. I could tell you everything if you would let me. I'm your dad, don't you want to see me again? You never visited me in there, after all those months. (sighing) Please get back soon.

Are you sure you would like to delete (36) messages?

Messages deleted.

# Fixing a Whole

**DANIELA CEJA**, Grade 12, Age 18. Oswego High School, Oswego, IL.
Erin Holtz, *Educator*

Mr. Smith had been fixing a hole for the past ten years. Relatively round and small in size, it sat askew above an empty bed—a bed whose sheets were a horrific shade of dandelion yellow. Mrs. Smith, however, had always liked those sheets, for they had belonged to her mother once. But now, those sheets horrified her too. She was constantly washing and drying them. The color—still horrific—had faded. But while the sheets were hanging from rotten clothespins outside, Mrs. Smith would watch her husband work. Every day. For ten years.

It must be noted that Mr. Smith was not a handyman. He was a man of the written word, his only tool a pen. He studied and earned his doctorate in anthropology, his interests mostly in the study of ancient linguistics. He was even a respected professor at one point, but that was all in the past—he had a hole to fix now. So, every morning for the past ten years, Mr. Smith would wake up (to his dismay), wear one of the two pairs of plaster-stained jeans he owned (to his wife's dismay), and trudge into the garage to retrieve his putty knife, wallboard, and other materials.

He would walk into the room where the smell of paint and lavender never seemed to leave. Then, he would begin fixing.

It's Sunday morning and a low hum of crackling jazz floats around the empty halls as Mr. and Mrs. Smith sit in silence. The only sounds that of Miles Davis and wall scraping. Mrs. Smith taps her right heel against the hardwood floor in cohesive rhythm with the music. She hadn't danced in ages. Part of her wanted to.

"Jim?"

He doesn't look at his wife, "Hm?"

"This song was played at our wedding." Mrs. Smith stares down at her acrylic nails—they're peeling away.

"Yes, I suppose so." He would always say that—he supposed everything about anything. Mrs. Smith rolls her eyes.

"The sheets are probably dry by now. I should go check on them."

"Yes, I suppose you should," he mutters, glasses slipping down the bridge of his nose. Mrs. Smith floats downstairs with the music.

*** 

Mr. Smith had covered the hole. They sit around the fireplace now. Mrs. Smith is reading a Victorian novella and Mr. Smith is reading an old newspaper. In fact, the same newspaper he has been reading for the past ten years. The crackling of the fire is the only noise exchanged between the two. It's warm.

Suddenly, Mr. Smith clears his throat, "They're finally fixing the potholes off Route 81."

"Are they now?" Mrs. Smith fakes interest—the holes had been fixed for ten years now.

"Yes, I suppose they are. About time too."

Mrs. Smith puts down her book and studies her husband. He's starved—his body is skinny and his mind is a prune. He's the product of something left in the dryer too long—shriveled, wrinkled, and small.

"I'm leaving," she says, lips forced into a perfect line. "Tomorrow."

This wasn't the first time she had threatened to leave him, nor would it be the last. Mrs. Smith liked seeing what her husband's reaction would be, or rather, if it would ever change. Tonight was no different.

"Where are you going?" he asks, eyebrows raised.

Some days it was Tallahassee, other days it was Alaska. She had even tried Australia once.

"New Orleans." Her eyes narrow on a Louis Armstrong album perched against their rusty record player.

Mr. Smith smiles. "That's a fine city, I suppose."

She feels like a balloon slowly deflating. "Yes," she murmurs, "I suppose."

She would never actually leave, though. Part of her wanted to.

\*\*\*

Mrs. Smith had been poking a hole for the past ten years. She would poke, prod, and tear the fresh plaster until the hole was back to its original size. She would often weep as she did so. Her mother's ugly yellow sheet would lay below her as she sat against her son's bed. Mrs. Smith would cry, but make no noise—the sounds of crackling fire and jazz would drown her out, anyways.

Tonight was no different.

She picks and tears and picks until the only plaster left is underneath her acrylic nails. When she's done, she sits with her back propped up against the wooden headboard. She wipes the tears away from the bags under her eyes. Her mascara is everywhere.

Mr. Smith walks in on his wife crying, "Mary? What's wrong?"

Mrs. Smith looks at her husband through glossy, blue eyes. He's distorted, blurry—unrecognizable. She pretends, for a moment, he's someone else.

"You won't grow old with me, Jim," she stammers through muffled sobs. "You're stuck, and I don't know how to get you unstuck."

Mr. Smith just stares. He sits on the edge of the bed and the yellow sheets wrinkle beneath him. Silence envelops them both for a while. Mr. Smith catches himself staring at the bullet hole above his son's bed.

Finally, he speaks, "Why would you rip out the plaster? I had just fixed that, Mary."

She runs her nose against the sleeve of her shirt. "I don't know." But she does. And she's told him countless times over—now, Mrs. Smith is tired.

"We have to move on someday," Mr. Smith sighs. "This is no way for any soul to live."

Part of her believes him. She nods.

"I miss him," she admits in a small, small voice.

Mr. Smith smiles, "I suppose I do too."

***

Mr. Smith wakes up and puts on one of the two pairs of plaster-stained jeans he owns. He walks out into the garage and gathers his putty knife, wallboard, and other materials. Mrs. Smith puts her mother's horrifically yellow sheets in the wash. Jazz floats through the empty halls.

It's Sunday morning. It's always Sunday morning.

Mr. Smith begins fixing.

# The Waves

**SIMONE GULLIVER**, Grade 11, Age 16. Montclair Kimberley Academy, Montclair, NJ. Eric Salehi, *Educator*

The girl you love moves like a whirlpool, each twist and turn of her figure sending sheets of water cascading toward the shore. You can feel the ripple of her currents from miles away, the force of them pulling you closer and closer, and when she grabs your wrist, you let her drag you under.

She never tells you her name. Not when the dancing is over and the beer cans are empty, not even when the weed's been smoked and the cherry-red of her lipstick bleeds permanently into your pillowcase. She leaves you like a whisper, like the sighs you'd pulled from her lips only hours before, floating breathless and silently out into the world.

You feign sleep while she dresses, pretending to hold a body that no longer occupies the space beside you; only the sunlight remains to drape itself across your back. Your eyes are closed and your head rests heavy on your shoulders, still waterlogged from last night's bad decisions, but you can hear her footsteps in the hallway, the soft clicking of the front door lock sliding back into place. You could've said something to her, you could've asked her to stay. You could've but you didn't, and it's eating you up inside.

Though nameless, she is not a stranger; the profile of her face, at least, is familiar. She sits two rows in front of you on the express train most mornings, the one you take to Tuesday and Thursday lectures at noon. It's always a short ride, never longer than half an hour, and you pass the time by watching. Watching slender fingers turn the pages of the book open across her lap, watching her slump against the window when Homer and Hesiod can no longer hold her interest, watching her reflection blur with suburban hillsides and city lights as they pass you by, watching until she steps off the train and there is nothing to watch anymore.

She's never noticed you before. This does not surprise you. You've spent a lifetime hiding in the periphery and vanishing into open spaces. You're the child who spied on his parents through holes in the wall, the boy who picked up other people's secrets like spare change dropped on the pavement. You are nowhere and everywhere all at once.

She doesn't recognize you. Not until almost a week later, when you catch her laughing quietly to herself at the middle-aged man talking far too loudly into his phone. You can't stop yourself from laughing too, and when she hears your voice she immediately turns around to face you, something like curiosity in her gaze. Hesitantly, she sticks her hand out across the empty row between you, pale arm extended for shaking, and in the train's dim lighting her skin gleams like porcelain.

You get a name this time, a proper introduction with everything she withheld the last time. Let's start over she says, let's pretend none of that ever happened, let's begin anew. And although you want nothing more than to return to the way things were seven nights ago, you lie through your teeth, fixing your lips into a smile and telling her it's all water under the bridge.

She invites you to a party. It's a Friday night, and you're following her directions to a rave somewhere down the shore, in a clifftop house beaten and battered by the ocean spray from waves below. There are people and they are everywhere, sipping piss-poor beer from Solo cups, lounging in half-broken lawn chairs, spilling out through the doorway and onto the deck. You join the kids inside, the ones packed together like fishes roped up in great, big hulking nets, the sequined dresses of pretty girls, gleaming like scales in the sunlight. Here the air feels sticky in your lungs, like there isn't enough of it to take in with each breath, but at least you're far away from the windowsills and the deck and the views of high tide's murky waters crashing against the cliffside beneath you.

The booze flows freely here. Cup after cup and can after can, you chug until your blood runs thick with courage, until the drop to the shore doesn't terrify you so much anymore, until your head spins and your vision blurs at the edges and your heart's sending you out on cliff-side excursions though your legs wobble like the stilts of this house when you walk on them.

The sun's already begun to set by the time you find your way back to sea level, winding down hillsides and sparsely pebbled walking paths in your search for solid ground. From here you can make out the railway tracks off in the distance, and when the thrumming of engines gets louder and louder, when the warning cry of an air horn pierces the air, you step up to the picket fence at the base of the cliffs and wave drunkenly to the trains flying by, specks of light careening toward nothing and nowhere.

She doesn't find you until much later, when the stars have made themselves known in the darkness above and the nighttime cold nips at your cheeks. You sit tangled up in one another on the sand-covered rocks of a stranger's backyard, the two of you blowing smoke rings under summer skies, tracing made-up constellations with unlit cigarettes from the pack of Marlboros in your pocket. She tells you stories about Perseus and Andromeda, Orion and the Pleiades, about heroes the Gods loved and heroes they did not and the weight of eternity in this bleak, bleak world. You fall asleep to the cadence of her voice, the way it ebbs and flows like waves lapping and crashing against these moonlit shores, and you think you'd let them swallow you whole if she asked you to. You're in love with her. It's going to kill you.

You wake up first and she follows. There's something methodical about the way she unwinds herself from you, uncurling fingers from handholds and detaching your limbs from hers with a certain, calculated grace. You watch as she walks back toward the house, the white skirt of her dress billowing in the seaside breeze, and you wonder why she doesn't understand. Why doesn't she understand how much you love her? How do you make her understand? How do you make her understand how much you love her?

You offer to drive her home. You can tell she doesn't want to get in the car with you. It's written all over the way she looks up to see if there's anyone else around who could take her, checks her phone to see if there's anyone else she could call to pick her up. But there's no cell service here, the nearest tow station miles away, and if she wants to get home by nightfall, you're all she's got.

She reluctantly pulls open the passenger door, the two of you sitting in silence as you turn your key in the ignition and pull out onto the road. She barely says a word, slumped against the windowpane, only ever moving to fiddle with the stations on the radio. It's been forty minutes of this, and you can't take it anymore.

"I love you," you say, rolling to a stop at the red light.

"Thank you." She still won't look at you. Why won't she look at you?

"Thank you? That's all you have to say?"

"It's the only thing I can say to you honestly," she says, picking at a grass stain on her dress. The stoplight changes to green and your car jerks forward as you slam your foot down on the gas.

"Do you have any idea how long I've been wanting to tell you that?"

"I'm sorry." She pulls a loose thread from the hem of her skirt. "What do you want me to say?"

"I don't know, maybe that you love me too?"

"You want me to lie to you?"

"Why does it have to be a lie?"

Finally, finally, she turns to look at you. This is it, you think. This is the moment you've been waiting for, the one where she finally realizes just how much you mean to her.

But gone is the tenderness you expected to see in her gaze; she doesn't reach out to take your hand or kiss your cheek. Instead her face is hardened, eyes glazed over with something like anger, fists balled tightly in her lap.

"You want the truth?" she asks, stare boring bullet holes into your forehead, smoking, smoldering, hot enough to singe and burn.

"Here's the fucking truth. You're a creep. Always watching pretty girls on the train, concocting some sick fantasy about how we're gonna fall in love and get married or some shit like that. Christ, you don't even know me. I bet you couldn't even tell me my favorite color if I asked you to."

You can and you do.

"Blue, it's blue."

"Jesus, you're insufferable. I never should've brought you

here. This is what being nice gets people I guess."

"How can you say that? How can you even say that?" Something wet rolls down your cheek. You're crying. When did you start crying?

"I can't deal with this," she says, unbuckling her seat belt. "Stop the car, I'm getting out."

She wants to leave. You can't let her leave.

"I told you to stop the car."

You don't hear her; the waves are roaring too loudly in your ears.

"What are you doing? You fucking missed the turn."

You didn't see it; you're too busy staring at the dashboard, watching the speedometer's needle push past ninety, then one hundred, and then beyond.

"Slow down, you need to slow down or we're gonna crash . . . Didn't you hear me? We're going to crash . . . Stop the car, stop the car, stop the car, STO—"

The car shoots past the metal fencing at the rock's edge, and you reach for her hand as the force of it sends you flying into the sun. You are Icarus, the boy with stars in his eyes and fire at his back, the boy who wanted too much and paid for it dearly, careening off a cliff to nothing and nowhere, colliding with the waves that once lapped and licked at your knees.

# Breaking and Entering

**JEEHWAN KIM**, Grade 9, Age 15. Choate-Rosemary Hall School, Wallingford, CT. Travis Feldman, *Educator*

"Isn'tya'gonna fight back?" he shouted.

The Kid could clearly make out the shape of the underside of his jaw but could not understand his summons to fight. He was becoming accustomed to the ritual. Soon there was no suspense. Only physical pain. The hot feeling running along his spine had since turned to ash.

"Please," he repeated, and the man walked away.

One day when he was being beaten, the burly Irishman held him close, briefly, his arms pressed around the Kid's throat. The Irishman smelled of coal dust and herring. They all smelled of coal dust and herring, but this was something different. There was a brief moment when he could smell his breath but the Irishman released him quickly, claimed that the Kid had insulted his wife.

The woman was not his wife. Not even his family.

In the evening, once again, the Kid fell asleep beside the child whom he suspected of stealing his father's pocket watch. He had begun inventorying his possessions ritualistically by the first light of morning, laying them out in a small pile in the corner of the hold where he made his nest.

He held the child close to his frail chest. He no longer cared about being robbed.

The flooring had been abraded to the color of honey from where the Kid had constantly lain against the floor shaking in the night.

In the third week, the English shippers threw three more corpses overboard. Two men who had succumbed to the choleric disease, the skin beneath the ridges of their cheekbones like bloated fish. The other victim was a young girl who had been carved down to nothing more than a rind of skin before ceasing to breathe.

By the middle of the third week, the bread was tasteless and his body was so wrung for fluid that urinating had been reduced to once a day, nights sleeplessly occupied by the shrill cries of the infants. His body became a rag; the fighting became slower and more habitual.

He stopped feeling any sort of malice toward the Irishman. He felt only a vindictive sense of duty. As though he was watching the entire thing unfold from above, no more involved than a spectator. There was no feeling in his hands at the end of the day.

He repeated the same phrase to himself in his native language as he lay by the rocking hull of the craft in his tiny territory: *ucidere*. He was uncertain of whether he would actually be able to commit the capital sin. By the early morning, the thrashing gale of winter rain drowned out the percussive thoughts in his head. For two whole days, none went above deck, fearing the third great green gale. The holds smelled of urine and herring and mildew and rot.

When, once again, the skies cleared, the Irishman punished the Kid with a wallowing physical rejoinder. Yet the Kid got in two solid blows to the man's kidney before being toppled.

By the fourth week, it was unclear whether they fought because they didn't understand each other, or didn't understand each other because they fought. At first the fighting was due to no rational cause. It was the raging hunger that had clawed its way through their skins. A gaseous infection. But by now it had become a ballet—simply a continuation of fights past.

The Irishman waved his hands in front of his head ceremoniously in a strange choreography when he fought. It resembled the small crustaceans that the Kid remembered pulling from the tidewater pools as a child.

The Kid learned how to fight too—his form simply a negative to the profuse ballistic style of the Irishman. Learned to anticipate the swinging blows. It was a consumptive pattern that soon passed the realm of vindication.

By the fifth week, they were forced to throw all of their salted provisions overboard because the lack of drinking water had driven them mad. There was simply no way to quench the thirst. His urine turned a bronzed yellow and only grew darker day by day.

And then something changed. In the fifth week, the Irishman had begun to lose weight. His brow and arms were speckled with sweat. His eyes were two small globes in a wooden mask. He spat blood twice in their usual match. One time the Kid almost knocked him over.

At night the treacherous child came to him and muttered through his sour breath the following word: g'night. It was the fourth phrase in the English language the Kid committed to mastery. The fifth one was what the child said next: g'luck.

The next morning, the English merchants changed coins between their hands once again. They had begun watching the Kid closely. They chewed on plugs of tobacco the color of wet leather.

Finally, he beat the Irishman. It was a foolish fight. The Irishman had been made weak by the parasitic disease—eyes ringed, face lightened. His confetti of clothing barely clinging to his cadaverous frame.

The Kid knew that he would win once the Irishman, whose eyes were wider than gun bores, muttered the single word. The Kid knew that he would win the fight when his opponent muttered this word:

"Please," he said, slowly, his teeth red.

It was the lasting token of the English language that, like a coin, would be weathered and tossed within his mind.

He continued pounding the Irishman on the side of his head, the man's body noticeably lighter. The entire ship gathering to watch in somber procession, even the English captain and his first admiral. They were savagely bored with the voyage.

The Kid's own limbs were lighter than those of a wooden marionette. The visions of his homeland were rapidly conjured. Scrawled in retinal blood on the back of his eyes. And then very quickly he beat the man's head against the wooden deck of the ship. It split like a soft melon.

In the evening, they rolled his stiff gray body off the hull of the boat. It disappeared quickly. The English privateers allowed the rest of the rations to be consumed in the final day of the voyage.

In the morning, all of the passengers rose onto the deck, cheering. They watched as the luminous shore drew closer, beginning as only a pebble and growing into a towering mass.

The Kid watched the emerald cloth of the ocean receding. He looked over the bow and saw blackened buildings and land. He looked into the sky and saw screaming white birds.

This was America.

# Burial

**TY KIATATHIKOM**, Grade 12, Age 17. Auburn High School, Rockford, IL.
Leslie Arbetman, *Educator*

Half of the house remained charred black, while the other half
had finally been repaired, the tiling portion of the roof fully
replaced and its shingles painted a fresh, pure white, so that
the whole building looked like the victim of a skin transplant
gone wrong.

"It's a shame, isn't it?" lamented my mother, lighting a cigarette as she eyed the blackened half of the house. "He would
have had that fixed by now."

"What's shameful," I said, "is that we're late." The service
had already begun; I could hear the chanting from inside the
car.

I found a place to kneel in the back of the main room. Used
for any and all of the *wat*'s (temple's) services, it was little more
than a large rectangle with sprinklers on the ceiling and tapes-
tries strewn across the walls. Sticks of incense burned in cups
of uncooked rice in order to mask the stench of fresh plaster.

I bowed my head, along with everyone else, to the three
monks seated on the platform before the statue of the Bud-
dha. They were reciting ancient Sanskrit verses, and all of the

men, women, and children prostrate in the room were singing it back to them. I joined in, adding my own small voice to the large, somber chorus.

As the service came to an end, the eldest of the monks stood and spoke while the other two prepared the brass bowl of holy water and the wooden brush. One of the younger monks stood with brush and bowl in hand. I braced, not for the water, but for the words I knew were about to come. I noticed how my mother was bracing as well, in her own way, for impact—how she was steeling her gaze, even though the only thing she was looking at was the floor.

"But above all, we can never forget," the elder decreed, his face darkening, one hand pressed against his bare, gray chest, "the losses we have incurred, and the sacrifices that certain souls have made for us all."

I felt at once the unmistakable chill that comes with being watched, like a million needles were piercing my skin all at the same time. It was the consequence of having survived.

The monk holding the bowl of water descended from the platform. He shook the brush above the heads of the waiting congregation as he passed by, allotting a few drops of water to the hair of each man, woman, and child. He chanted softly as he walked. My mother trembled. I kept her in the corner of my vision, bating my breath, wishing I could hold her. I didn't.

After the ritual was over, all of the families presented their laundry baskets and hampers full of offerings to the monks, and I walked out into the field to watch the children play for a while.

Separated from the other children, sequestered under the shadow of an elm tree, knelt a Lao girl with a flower in her braids. I could see that she was holding something.

"Why don't you show me what you have there?"

After some hesitation, she obeyed, turning around to reveal rich crimson stains on the skirt and stomach of her *sinh*. She was cradling the corpse of a bird in her arms. A robin, from the look of it. It had a broken wing, the skin of it exposed where feathers should have been. Its neck was limp. Its beak was open wide. Blood trickled slowly from its two closed, peaceful eyes.

"What happened?" I asked.

"The boys," she replied. She kept her head down as she spoke. Her voice was haunting and small. "My brothers, they . . ."

"They what?"

"It was perched," she went on, fighting back tears, "in the tree. They were throwing stones at it. For fun. I told them to stop, and they laughed at me. But it's not their fault—"

She looked down at the bird, broken and dead.

"They didn't think they would actually hit it."

I unbuttoned my shirt and wrapped it around the bird, taking it off of her and setting it on the ground beside the trunk of the elm. I wiped my hands on my T-shirt and surveyed the field. Children were still playing. Fathers were still smoking. Mothers were still inside. Clouds were gathering overhead.

"I'll be right back."

I went back to the barn and rummaged around in the attic until I found a shovel, then returned to the Lao girl and began digging a hole in the space between two great roots of the tree.

After some time passed, she said, "Can I ask you a question?"

"What is it?"

"That shovel," she began, carefully measuring her words. "Was it his?"

I worked on widening the hole, saying nothing.

"Um, your dad's, is what I meant."

"No," I answered. "It belongs to the *wat*."

"But he used it, didn't he? I thought I saw him once—"

"Yeah. He was the groundskeeper."

"What's that mean?"

"He took care of things."

I struck the ground hard with the shovel. Pieces of smashed earth soiled my pants and shoes. Her mouth opened like she was going to say something, but she didn't. When the hole was deep enough, she picked up the bird and placed it inside. I filled the hole back up and flattened the dirt with the back of the shovel.

When we were finished, we sat down under the tree. The creature lay resting in the space between the two of us, my shirt its burial shroud, the hole its shallow grave.

"Would you like to say some words?" I asked half-heartedly.

"Your hands are dirty," she said.

She was right. They were caked in dirt.

"So are yours," I said. She inspected her own, as if noticing for the first time the blood drying on them, her arms, and her *sinh*.

It began to rain.

# A Satire on Suburbia

**ANI FREEDMAN**, Grade 12, Age 17. Bethlehem Central High School, Delmar, NY. Eileen Turo, *Educator*

Dear fellow Haswell Farms Homeowner's Association members,
It's me, Linda, just checking in and providing my weekly suggestions to improve the neighborhood and create a better environment for our children.

A new family has just moved in on Hasgate Drive, so I think it's our job to make them feel welcomed and show them the Haswell way!

Catherine will be placing our flyer, "48 Helpful Recommendations for Contributing to Haswell Farms in a Productive Way," in their mailbox this Wednesday at 7 a.m. Sandra will photocopy our compiled eight-page list of all 62 of the various allergies our children have in the neighborhood to ensure their cookies or Rice Krispie treats don't poison our little angels at our annual Fourth of July parade. Janet, make sure you've added Jalen's gluten sensitivity and Jessyka's intolerance of anything nonorganic. I am assigning Diane and Teresa to drive by their house at least three times a day to ensure that their yard is up to the standards that Terri and I came up with after the fiasco that was the Smith house on Barrington Court. I hope Jeff has learned what a danger growing roses is now;

those thorns nearly scratched my son when we were doing our daily power walk/neighborly check-in.

Your favorite HOA president,

Linda

HOA members and parents:

It seems our new neighbors aren't fully aware of how things work in our special little corner of Bethlehem. While doing my usual rounds at 9:35 a.m. and 12:15 p.m., I drove by the new family's home only to find that they had placed their garbage cans on the right side of the driveway rather than the left. Clearly, they have not read the Haswell Handbook, which distinctly requires all garbage cans to be placed on the left side of the driveway as to maintain order on the streets and not confuse the simple garbage men, who probably don't speak English (one of their names is "Joe"—I believe it's pronounced "Hoe"). But it's important not to be too quick to judge them yet. It would be fantastic if someone would just give them a friendly reminder of how we do things in our serene Delmar setting.

Thanks again!

Linda

Homeowner's Association:

Has no one been paying attention to my previous emails regarding Haswell's newest family?? Am I the only one concerned for the safety of our children? Yesterday, at approximately 3:17 p.m. (according to my log), the teenage son was standing outside in a group, like some sort of gang meeting on his front porch. Instinctively, I pulled out my binoculars from my Vera Bradley handbag to get a closer look. They appeared to be playing some sort of card game, with the name "Magic" written in big letters across a box next to them. Clearly, this was some sort of gambling-séance combination. Absolutely horrifying! I furiously marched right up to the door, scattering their devil cards. I knocked on the door, which incidentally caused my Pandora bracelet to go flying. The mother answered the door, and I gave her a very important speech about proper behavior for teenagers, as my Tommy and Krystyn are perfect examples to follow. How can we allow this family's ignorance to continue?

Linda

Fellow concerned parents of the HOA:
I have received a large number of emails from all of you regarding my most recent actions. However, I am wondering where all of your input was last week when I sent my initial email. Too busy "helping" Cale with his college applications, huh, Francine? We all know that boy doesn't give a rat's ass about trying to help starving children in Africa, so stop lying about his "life-changing" experience while on vacation in Morocco in that essay. Nevertheless, I understand how worried you all must be. I am too. It had been brought to my attention—via the security cameras I placed at every street corner—that Haswell's newest troublemaker has been driving through the neighborhood and congregating with his pesky friends past 8:30 p.m. Based on past behavior, there is only one conclusion to be drawn: These are devil-worshipping, gambling, anal-sex-addicted drug dealers we are dealing with. Of course, I notified the police of the illegal activity taking place at the household, and how they must be "dropping gates," the new term for manufacturing heroin with intent to distribute. Worried the teenagers may have gotten wind of the anonymous tip and hid the substances before the authorities could arrive, I acquired eight grams of cocaine and stashed it in the teen's car. Anyway, you are all welcome for ridding the neighborhood of this teenage menace.

Hope all is well,

Linda

# How to Look More Asian: A Guide to Becoming an Exotic Geisha or Your Favorite K-pop Star

**EMILY JIANG**, Grade 10, Age 15. High Technology High School, Lincroft, NJ. Sandra Ascari, *Educator*

### For Ladies

1. Shortcuts: If you are Scarlett Johansson, Emma Stone, or Tilda Swinton, skip to step 11.

2. Body: Asian beauty is fragility. Use a Chinese porcelain doll as a model. Exquisite Asian girls are thin, delicate, and flat. Paint your face yellow, like jaundice, then apply generous rouge and a thin line of red lipstick for contrast.

3. Hair: Dye your hair black and straighten it. The hair can either be parted in the middle and let loose or gathered in a regal bun atop the head like that of an ancient empress.

4. Eyes: Asians have small, narrow, and slanted eyes. To achieve this exotic Oriental appearance, begin by relaxing your eyelids, as if you are slowly falling asleep. The technique should morph your double eyelids into a classic Asian monolid.

You should further intensify this effect by looking down, an action which may better highlight the natural submissiveness of Asian females or suggest that you are another one of those nerds engrossed in your studies. See steps 7 and 8, respectively, for further information.

5. Selfie: Crack a close-lipped smile and flash a peace sign (remember, palm facing outward!). If you can get somebody else to take your picture, you should incorporate a tourist squat as well, with a Canon camera dangling from your neck. Remember to jabber in nonsensical Chinese to provoke angry side glances from the locals that will truly complete the look.

6. Empowerment: Asian females are either nerds, China dolls, or infamous Tiger Mothers. If you are currently a student, see step 8. If you are no longer a student but do not have children, see step 9. If you have children, you fall under the Tiger Mom category regardless of whether or not you are a student as well—see step 9.

7. Nerd: Tuck your hair back into a ponytail. Find a pair of glasses that are plain, unassuming, and utterly devoid of style. A spatter of pimples and maybe some applied grease (pay YouTube a visit for a makeup tutorial if you aren't contending with the Great Firewall) makes it more convincing as well. Throw on a pair of baggy jeans and a random wrinkled T-shirt—you know, the ones you get for free that say New York Philharmonic or Field Day 2010 or the ones you get from nerd events that boast MATHCOUNTS Nationals 2015 or Scholastic Art & Writing Awards. Top it off with a hoodie proclaiming your position as captain of the school's varsity chess team. If you can't decide on a surname to embroider on the back, "Wang" is always a good choice.

8. China doll: Keep only two words in mind—submissiveness and fragility. To become one of those dainty geisha

girls, follow steps 2 through 4 above and add accessories. You can find Chinese hand fans and embroidered lace umbrellas on sketchy online websites. When talking to others, speak quietly and shyly and cast your gaze downward with the sad elegance of a wilting lotus flower.

9.  Tiger Mother: Do you have children? Would you like for them to become the next Albert Einstein or perhaps be a piano virtuoso? Then hopefully this guide will help you unleash your inner Tiger Mother! Wear itchy sweaters from the clearance rack at Target, do your weekly shopping at Costco, and keep your hair in a bun tighter than the fine line of your lips. You worry only about your children, for their futures are your future. Tiger Mom means tough love. It means gritting your teeth and giving the bamboo feather duster treatment to your child because he/she has received a B, a Bad grade, an aBomination, an Asian fail. It means three hours of piano and violin practice every day and Kumon work sheets. It means no dating, no sleepovers, no playdates, no friends. Rest in peace, your child's social life.

10.  Language: The Asian language consists of inscrutable characters painted on hanging scrolls and is read right-to-left or in some other strange, foreign orientation. A helpful tip to sound Asian at least to non-Asians (I mean, that's all we're going for here, right?) is to use two-word phrases that rhyme with "ding dong." (Notable examples include ching chong and ping pong.)

11.  Accent: Native speakers of the Asian language speak accented English, having just recently emigrated from Asia (escaping sweatshop conditions and communist regimes on a rickety bamboo raft adrift in the vast open ocean). To sound Fresh Off the Boat™, use articles (a, an, the) where they aren't needed, and skip articles where they should be used.

All instances of the letter *L* should be pronounced as if they are instead the letter *R*, such as in herro and Engrish.

### For Gentlemen

1. Shortcuts: If you are Matt Damon, Warner Oland, or Mickey Rooney, skip to step 10.

2. Body: Never go outside. Never play sports. Never lift any weight heavier than a textbook. Flat is a good shape to be in because textbooks are flat, and textbooks are good. (There's a reason the Bible is a book and not a football.) Walk with a slouch. Your mind is on fluid force calculations and linear algebra, not on your spine.

3. Hair: Sport (even if you're unathletic) the classic "bed head" look. Should you ever be so caught up in mental calculations that you trip and fall, your messy, matted mop of hair should cushion, if not your dignity, at least your precious cerebellum.

4. Face: You can never go wrong with painting your face yellow—it's an instant step toward looking Asian! As for your eyes, all that should be seen at the top of your face are goggle-like glasses perched atop your textbook-flat nose. Don't forget the grubby, three-inch-thick lenses.

5. Dress: See step 7 under For Ladies. Nerds are nerds.

6. You should now be ready to present yourself to the world as another one of those Asian Nerds™! If you find yourself cornered in a grungy alleyway by a crowd chanting "nerd, nerd"—fret not! It's the perfect opportunity to display your kung fu techniques and terrify the haters. Remember: wax on, wax off, with a flying Bruce Lee kick in between.

7. Mental preparation: If you've adhered to the procedure to become an authentic Asian nerd, there are still some things to bear in (your overpowered, oversized) mind. Prepare to

never date. Prepare to live your angsty adolescent ages with no girl ever eyeing you for anything other than a plea for the answers to last night's math homework. It's a way of life you must accept as soon as possible. It's a compromise.

8. Are you over 35 years of age? Sorry, you've lost your chance to be a K-pop star (see step 12), but you can just settle for being a nerdy dad instead. (You know, one of those dads who passionately discusses physics at the dinner table, builds robots and programs Raspberry Pi instead of watching *Keeping Up With the Kardashians,* and mixes Coca-Cola with antacids in a kitchen tumbler just to "see what happens.") You can keep the careless hair and thick glasses from the previous steps.

9. K-pop star: These idols are overtaking the media! Becoming one of these boys, who have captured the hearts of millions, may seem an elusive aspiration, but as long as you're young enough, a few simple steps is all it takes. Adopt a mushroom haircut, the coiffure that bobs like an overeager dog around your forehead. Dress in tight, shiny black pants and a suit for a classy semblance. Teenage girls will pine for you, their faces alight with adoration and idolatry. Even straight boys might admire the gleam of your photoshopped skin and the way your hairdo flops up and down like medusae with your every step. When you reach 35 years of age, see step 8.

10. Wrapping it up: Embrace your yellowface! For the K-pop stars . . . enjoy the affection while it lasts. Meanwhile, our hearts go out to the nerds, who may never know love. But hey! You're always welcome to try the tactic of calling "Lingling" in the streets—someday, it just might work!

**LAUREN WHITE**, *In the Woods*, Drawing & Illustration. Grade 12, Age 17, Ft. Hayes Arts & Academics High School, Columbus, OH. Anna Bory-Ackers, *Educator*

# Unqualified: A Women's Glossary

**SHAUN-MARLEY DUNCAN**, Grade 12, Age 17. Berkeley Carroll School, New York, NY. Rafael Sanchez, *Educator*

*I'm sorry*
The words you learn to use the most, an apology for your breasts, vagina, and hips.
*Bitch*
The consequence of you not apologizing for the space you take up.
*I'm not sure but the answer could be . . .*
What you say in math class, even though you are one hundred percent sure of what the answer is.
*50 point—*
How much of the answer you actually end up getting to give before one of the male students in your class cuts you off.
*Miffed*
The way you feel after this happens; annoyed, but this happens every day and you don't want to make it a "thing."
*A thing*
What happens when you "overreact" to a situation.

**Emotion**
Something you never know how much of to show.

**Know-it-all**
Something you learn in first grade that you do not want to be, even though you think knowing it all sounds a heck of a lot better than knowing nothing.

**Know-nothing**
1. Something that you are called in second grade because you now only answer questions in your head. 2. A phrase, in this case, that would really apply to the boys who called you that, because they know nothing about the fact that you got every question right.

**Actually**
Something that you have to say when you correct a man, e.g., I actually disagree, I think the answer is actually . . .

**Just**
1. The word you use when you consider the absurdity of what has transpired, e.g., Did that just happen?!? 2. A word that you will then use to undermine the values of your thoughts and opinions, e.g., I just think that I deserve to be treated as fairly as any of the male students in this class.

**Hands**
Something that covers your mouth more than they are raised in the air. 2. Things that must cover your mouth when you take a bite of food or attempt to express what you really think.

**Celery**
Something that in addition to sugar, spice, and everything nice, you are supposed to be made of because it has negative calories.

**Calories**
One of the only things that you are allowed to calculate.

**Calculations**
Something that you must do in every conversation so that
your words do not threaten the boys.
**Boys**
1. Will be boys and you don't have a choice. 2. The source of
some of the best bullshit you have ever heard.
**Bullshit**
What you think in your head when the boy in your class cuts
you off.
**Angry**
1. Something that you are not supposed to be. 2. Something
that the males in your life will call hormonal.
**Apology**
1. Something you will be forced to give when you get angry.
2. Something you do when a guy trips you on your way to the
bathroom. 3. Something that you are doing by shoving the
tampon up your sleeve.
**Period**
Something that you intend to end your sentences with.
**Question**
The upwards intonation you use at the end of all your state-
ments? Because if you sound certain of yourself, then you
might be on your period.
**Certainty**
Something you should not have . . . should you?
**Am I Making Sense?**
What you say when the Question is not enough. For example,
if I was explaining how to use qualifiers, I might end my ex-
planation with Am I Making Sense?

# Update to Community Regarding Rich White Liberal Suburban School District's Sky-High Test Scores

**MICHAEL CHENG**, Grade 12, Age 17. Lower Merion High School, Ardmore, PA. Christina Minecci, *Educator*

Dear Rich White Liberal Suburban School District Community, We are pleased to inform you that this year's PSSA scores, Keystone Exam scores, SAT scores, AP scores, ACT scores, IB scores, AMC scores, PSAT scores, PLAN scores, GMAT scores, GRE scores, MCAT scores, LSAT scores, DAT scores, and DRP scores have recently been released, and our school district has performed at the very top of all of these examinations. Specifically, our school district performed at the 99.99th percentile of all of these standardized tests, showing that our helicopter parents are among the most fiercely dedicated in the nation. Indeed, our helicopter parents have worked incredibly hard to organize college visits for middle schoolers, shepherd their children to expensive summer test-preparation programs, and introduced our kids to sports that everyone in America plays, such as fencing, squash, lacrosse, and rowing, which will make them even more recruitable by highly regarded universities such as Stanford, Harvard, Yale, and Princeton . . . did I just hear Arizona State? Yikes. Sorry, but that's a community college.

We are incredibly proud of our students' hard work and achievements. Notwithstanding the fact that our school district's median household income is $160,000 per year, and that students from the richest ten percent of families score an average of 300 points better on the SAT than students from the poorest ten percent of families, we are incredibly honored to have a districtwide average SAT score of 1409 out of 1600. This SAT score proves that our students are not only learning, but can also apply what they learn in school to real-world challenges, such as filling in hundreds of bubbles with a number 2 pencil under a strict time limit, and knowing to guess C, not A.

In particular, we would like to congratulate junior Ricky Morton, who after paying $800 per hour for a private SAT tutor and studying for the SAT since fourth grade, scored an impeccable 1600 out of 1600 on the SAT exam. Well done, Ricky. Your parents must be so incredibly proud of this achievement that you worked for all on your own. We know that you will do great things in life, starting with getting into Dartmouth College despite the fact that eight generations of your family went there. We know that you got into college on the basis of all of your hard work and dedication. After all, you went to Cancun on a service learning trip, where you built houses for needy tourists and lived in a house that didn't have an elevator for two weeks, truly learning what it's like to live in poverty. That means that you care about the community and you want to make a real impact on the world. You're definitely not following a path that your parents have put out in front of you since you were three.

Moving on to a different note, we would also like to honor seventh-grader Emily Blank, who is such a go-getter that her parents signed her up to take the SAT four years early. Emily, who scored an impressive 1470 out of 1600, with a full 800 on the math section and a 670 on the reading section, is a truly amazing student. Even though seventh-graders usually don't take the SAT, Emily proved that anyone can have helicopter parents who are so overbearing that they get their children to suffer through standardized testing four years early. Thanks, Emily!

Our students have also scored incredibly well on other standardized tests. This year, 86 percent of our students who took Advanced Placement exams passed with a score of 3, 4, or 5. To celebrate these students' accomplishments, we made a mural out of all of their AP score reports. As for the students who scored 2s and 1s: We hung their yearbook pictures on the Wall of Shame. The terrible parents of these failing students received phone calls from the guidance office urging them to do a better job at hovering over every femtosecond of their children's lives and received a letter in the mail instructing them to spend more money on private tutors and out-of-class instruction and less money on silly video games and movies for their kids.

We also did incredibly well on the ACT, which isn't even a real test. We averaged an ACT score of 33 out of 36 in spite of the fact that the only people who take the ACT are the people who don't do well on the SAT and whose parents still have another $15,000 sitting under a mattress somewhere to burn on another set of private tutors, Kaplan classes, and independent college counselors. This ACT score, which is a lot of points higher than the ACT score of the failing Philadelphia high school 5 miles away from us, proves to us that our children know how to choose the standardized test they can score higher on and impress colleges. Colleges aren't impressed by students who waste their time working at McDonald's after school; they're impressed by the ACT bigwigs who spend every day prepping for a multiple-choice test that will decide the direction and worth of their entire lives.

High-stakes standardized testing also features prominently in our elementary schools. Every one of our kindergarteners, first-graders, second-graders, third-graders, fourth-graders, and fifth-graders hunkered down last October to take the DRPs, which stands for Death by Reading Passages. We use the results of the DRP tests to determine who gets to move up to gifted education and who gets downgraded to special education, which definitely receives the exact same resources and respect from our college-focused community as gifted education does. The DRP tests are not the only standardized test we use to decide whether to doom a student to a life of mediocrity that will never get them into an Ivy League College. We also use the results from the PSSAs, a scientifically valid examination made by companies that definitely do not profit in any manner whatsoever from making the test, to determine whether students get placed in smart math or stupid math, because fourth-graders should be segregated by their academic ability from a very young age. We truly believe that we can assign every elementary school student a number that, when plugged into a complicated formula, can help us determine whether they deserve to be placed in challenging classes.

After leaving our school district, our graduates are prepared to succeed anytime success is measured by the number of bubbles one can fill in correctly under a strict time limit. Eighty-two percent of our graduates will take the GMAT, GRE, MCAT, LSAT, or DAP within four years of graduating from high school.

Over 95 percent of these graduates consistently rank among the 10 percent of undergraduates who still have money left to purchase more private tutors, classes, and summer camps to prepare for these very difficult examinations that cannot be gamed at all. These graduates definitely have aspirations for the future that extend beyond becoming a doctor, lawyer, or engineer and making, in the incredibly eloquent words of one of our most esteemed graduates, a "shitload of dough."

Of course, we do not only focus on standardized testing. As a rich, 80 percent white, liberal suburban school, we provide our students with all of the experiences and perspectives they need to truly understand why America is actually the most disgusting country in the world. Our AP United States History textbook takes care to recognize the contributions of every oppressed minority group in the country so that by the time our mostly white students graduate, they will know that they are privileged and will be able to relate to minority students without being even a little racist at all.

In fact, our school actually helps students truly understand, and not just pay lip service to, the dynamics of privilege and power in society. We give our students EXPO markers and posters so that they can make their own safe spaces, preparing them to succeed at a liberal top-tier college like Yale or Amherst. We give our students access to custom T-shirt machines so they can make T-shirts protesting those evil Republicans who don't live in a rich liberal bubble, and instead live in a rich Republican one. We even give our students free Beats earmuffs so they can ignore that One Obligatory Conservative Student at Every Liberal School in style.

Overall, our school district ranks among the top in the nation, and we intend to keep it that way. We encourage you to keep shepherding your children through a circus of extracurricular activities, music lessons, and organized sports teams starting from the moment they turn three years old. Make sure you sign your kids up for this deluge early, or else millions of other future-oriented helicopter parents will have done so before you and your kid will have absolutely no shot at getting into Princeton once high school comes around. Thank you so much for your time, and we look forward to preparing your children for the "real world" by teaching them how to succeed on multiple-choice tests and giving them completely authentic experiences with diversity.

Sincerely,

Dr. Jill F. Cash

President, Board of School Directors

Rich D. White

Superintendent

# Do Not Compare Me to a Summer's Day

**GABRIEL SÁNCHEZ AINSA**, Grade 12, Age 17. John Cooper School, The Woodlands, TX. Peter Elliott, *Educator*

## CHARACTERS

WILL    Melodramatic seventeen-year-old. He knows a lot of poetry and literature in general, which he keeps quoting throughout the play. He just met FLORA, with whom he immediately fell in love.

FLORA    Seventeen-year-old girl who just got admitted into Columbia. She just met WILL, this guy who looks kind of interesting and cute.

## SETTING
A park at night. The starry sky is the only light that illuminates the stage. WILL enters from the right.

WILL    Tonight it is the perfect night (looking at the sky)
   to have a date under the stars,
   but where is she, my one true love? (looking around)
   What shadow hides her from me?

[FLORA enters from the left.]

FLORA (smiling)   Hey, Will. I'm right here. So, hmm, I got your text to hang out tonight. So, what do you wanna do? Go to the movies? Bowling, maybe?

WILL   Let not those earthly pleasures blind
   our hearts from our heavenly love—

FLORA   So how about dinner?

WILL   —our stars have summoned us tonight,
   so that we can profess our love.
   Oh! Our love, that 'tis an ever-fixed mark!
   Come, gentle night. Come, loving, black-browed night,
   give me my sweet Flora. And when she shall die
   take her and cut her out in little stars,
   and she will make the face of heaven so fine
   that all the world will be in love with night
   and pay no worship to the garish sun.
   Oh, my Flora, I shall wait no more!
   I must ask you right now: (kneeling and taking out an
   engagement ring)
   Will you, my dearest, sweetest love,
   want to spend your life with me?
   Say yes, a thousand times yes,
   and we will wed tomorrow night!

FLORA (laughing)   Ha ha ha! That's one creative way to break the ice on a first date. What next? "Shall I compare thee to a summer's day?" (WILL looks at her seriously, and FLORA stops laughing abruptly.) Wait, you are kidding, right? Please, tell me that you are kidding. Please do not compare me to a summer's day.

WILL    A man in love would rather die
   than joke about his love.

FLORA (freaking out)    Oh my god! You are actually propos-
ing to me! This is freaking insane. You know, when I was putting on my makeup earlier today, I just thought I was going
on a date with this cute guy I met at Barnes & Noble! I never
imagined he was gonna turn out to be a psycho!

WILL    I am not insane but in love!
"Lovers and madmen have such seething brains,
Such shaping fantasies, that apprehend
More than cool reason ever comprehends.
The lunatic, the lover and the poet
Are of imagination all compact:
One sees more devils than vast hell can hold,
That is, the madman: the lover, all as frantic,
Sees Helen's beauty in a brow of Egypt:
The poet's eye, in fine frenzy rolling,
Doth glance from heaven to earth, from earth to heaven;
And as imagination bodies forth
The forms of things unknown, the poet's pen
Turns them to shapes and gives to airy nothing
A local habitation and a name."

FLORA    Holy crap, holy crap . . . You do realize that we just
met yesterday, right? We met YES-TER-DAY! You don't just
propose to people the day after you meet them.

WILL    Love's not time's fool, though rosy lips and cheeks
within his bending sickle's compass come—

FLORA    This is not making any sense anymore. Will, here, I
think I'm going to leave. My mom is calling me.

[FLORA pretends like someone is calling her on the phone and tries to leave, but WILL grabs her hand before she can leave. They look into each other's eyes.]

WILL (quickly)    Marissa is busy right now. Let's not bother her with our youthful passions.

FLORA    How do you know my mother's name?

WILL (ignoring her question)    Had we but world enough and time—

FLORA    Oh my god, not again.

WILL (putting his finger on her lips and shushing her)
  Let me finish—
  This coyness, lady were no crime.
    We would sit down and think which way
    To walk, and pass our long love's day.
    But at my back I always hear
    Time's winged chariot hurrying near.
    Thus, though we cannot make our sun
    Stand still, yet we will make him run.
[They gaze into each other's eyes in silence.]

FLORA    But, Will, I–I can't just marry you. I mean, I am going to Columbia, my parents wouldn't approve, I barely know you . . . And I think it may be illegal because, you know, we are seventeen.

WILL    Things growing are not ripe until their season;
    So I, being young, till now ripe not to reason.
    And touching now the point of human skill,
    reason becomes the marshal to my will
    and leads me to your eyes, where I o'erlook

love's stories written in love's richest book.

FLORA (blushing and smiling)   I mean, when you put it like
that . . . (aside and looking at the audience) And what do you
think? Yes, you, the audience. I need some life advice. I know
that he may seem just a little bit crazy and all, but I think
he actually loves me. And he's cute, he's smart, and he's very
passionate. And he's soo romantic. And, I don't know. When
I looked into his eyes (glances at him shyly) well, you know.
And yet, to say the truth, love and reason keep little company
together nowadays. What if he's the One?
    (to WILL) Oh, Will! I shall leave my current life,
    and leave my future that seems so bright,
    and tomorrow I shall be your new wife!
    So meet me here tomorrow night,
    and we shall intertwine our long-time fates
    in our second, yet so perfect, date!

WILL      Oh, Flora!

FLORA      Oh, Will!

   They hold hands and they exit.

# Letter to My Substitute

**TREVOR ZAVAC**, Grade 11, Age 17. Noblesville High School, Noblesville, IN. Bethany Zilligen, *Educator*

To My Substitute,

Hello, brave friend and substitute to my position of chief psychologist at Webster's Asylum for the Wrongly Afraid. I write this letter to inform you of some of the more worrisome patients who are residing with us in the hospital at the moment; all of whom have undergone some mildly traumatizing event that has not given them major psychological problems, but instead has given them an irrational fear of something they find in their daily life. They have not been mentally scarred, but mentally scratched; for example, a mailman may come in if he has an irrational fear of dogs, or a pilot with an irrational fear of heights. They normally come here for month-long intervals, but we sometimes require them to stay longer, depending on the severity or progression of their illness.

I have taken the time to write to you about the more severe cases we have, and to wish you good luck whilst I take my "sabbatical" in a far, far away place at a great distance from here and at a location that I wish not to disclose, as I will be completely out of contact while I am away. If you need to reach me (though I cannot understand why you would), you can try my cellphone, which will be broken.

Stanley Fitzpatrick:
One patient who may give you trouble is one who has resided with us for seven months: Stanley Fitzpatrick. Yes, he is the very same Fitzpatrick as the proprietor of the bakery on Main Street; however, Mr. Fitzpatrick's current state of mind is not permitting him to bake. You see, Mr. Fitzpatrick, an accomplished baker of bread and other leavened delicacies, has become extremely gluten intolerant. Like most people who have this intolerance, or fear, as I prefer it called, his illness is purely mental: He displays no physical symptoms to the consumption of any gluten product. Unlike those who typically possess this physical/mental illness, he is not a female around the age of twenty-five who possesses an abhorrence for her self-image, but instead a man the age of forty-five who was engulfed by bread dough during a mishap in his bakery. He was unable to escape for many hours because of the dough's strong protein that kept him locked in: gluten.

His illness is so severe that he cannot sit comfortably in a room that contains any type of bread, or even images of bread. Mr. Fitzpatrick is also unable to speak about, hear, or see locations that are commonly associated with bread, such as his bakery; other bakeries; words like *sourdough, white, monkey, corn,* and *wheat*; park benches in which elderly community members feed pigeons; and the nation of France. To counteract this fear, I have been slowly introducing him to the ideas in which bread and other baked goods are key. For example, to each of our weekly sessions, I wear a black beret and long-sleeved T-shirt with thick horizontal stripes, play accordion music instead of white noise in the background, and sit on the park bench that you will find in the corner of my office. I have not made any progress on getting him near cigarette smoke, however.

Garrick Watson:

Mr. Watson is the proud owner and operator of a tattoo parlor. He is quite skilled—a true artist, but he too has come into misfortune. As he was tattooing someone's arm, he tripped and accidentally impaled himself with the needle. Since this fiasco, he has been afraid of needles. The fear was manageable at first, and he coped with it for a while; but by the time he had come here, he was afraid of all sharp objects. He has even had trouble staying in the same room as his roommate, a *Jeopardy!* winner afraid of Alex Trebek, who has been described to him as being sharp. He does not eat in the cafeteria because people use knives and forks when they eat, and he cried the entire time during the hospital's movie night (when watching *Sleeping Beauty,* he found the scenes with the spinning wheel and Maleficent's horns to be most displeasing). He insists that everyone write with either dull crayons or markers and that they refrain from sewing or knitting while he is in the room.

To help him counteract this fear, we have been completing our sessions next to the blue spruce in the garden, and I have been writing with a newly sharpened pencil. During our sessions, I sit upon a very old chair that was poorly hammered together while chewing on a toothpick. He has been making good progress, but remember to keep your fingernails trimmed. On the off chance you do a session in my office, remember to remove the portrait of Otto von Bismarck in his military uniform.

Samuel Smith:
This poor man, a coroner for the local police, has what seems a rational fear of death; however, he is not afraid of dying himself, but afraid of people or plants that have died. A bad fear to have for a person who works with those who have passed on. This patient is making excellent progress. The only reason I include him in this list is to remind you to water my fern that sits by the window and be sure that the Venus flytrap on my desk stays healthy and upright.

Lindsay Snydell:
Ms. Snydell has been a wonderful dental hygienist for many years, but she recently underwent a midlife wisdom tooth removal, which rendered her afraid of oral surgeons and, tragically, dentists. She cannot stand next to a dentist or walk into his or her office without becoming extremely anxious.

To help this fear, have her lay down on my desk with my desk lamp shining onto her face. I also recommend scenting the room with mint or bubble gum before her entrance and wearing gloves during her session, as this should help to lower her anxiety when she returns to the workplace.

Also: I should make mention of the textile manufacturer who is afraid of blankets. He will be sleeping in the hallway each night.

That concludes the list of patients I fear, rather, patients who are troublesome. I tell you, dear friend, being in an asylum can drive one crazy.

I shall return when I get back. Thank you again for your help. And, most importantly, have fun.

Good luck,
Dr. William Morose

**CECILIA FARRAR**, *Opa's Chair*, Painting. Grade 12, Age 17, Lakota West High School, West Chester, OH. Stephanie Gauer, *Educator*

## ABOUT THE AUTHORS

**SALIHAH AAKIL** is a 15-year-old writer, artist, and entrepreneur. She is the co-founder of Salvage, a nonprofit charity. She is also a two-time DC Youth Poet Laureate finalist; an outspoken advocate for social justice; the Words, Beats, and Life 2017 Grand Slam Champion; and a Scholastic Awards National Medalist.

**GABRIEL SÁNCHEZ AINSA** was born and raised in Madrid, attended high school in Houston, and currently attends UChicago in Illinois, but he spends most of his time inside his head. He received a Scholastic Awards Silver Medal in Humor, which he uses to justify endlessly telling bad jokes.

**CHRISTOPHER BARLOW** is a rising junior at South Portland High School. He enjoys dogs, his friends, and the Grateful Dead.

**DANIEL BLOKH** is a 17-year-old writer living in Birmingham, Alabama, and the author of *Grimmening* (Diode Editions, 2018) and *Holding Myself Hostage in the Kitchen* (Lit City Press, 2017). He has been published in *The Kenyon Review, The Blueshift Journal, The Account, Permafrost*, and more.

After four years of being the editor of her school newspaper and learning about the way journalism projects voices across social boundaries and creates intimate human connections, **NEELAM BOHRA** is heading to college in hopes of becoming a journalist. She has spent years unsure of her future, but one thing has remained clear: She needs a career that allows her to help people. She cannot wait to fulfill this passion through communication.

**GEOFFREY BRANN** is a technology aficionado who spends every free moment on his computer. He is deferring his admission to Cornell (where he plans to study computer science) to spend next year in Nepal and Madagascar, where he will be completely unplugged and offline. He is looking forward to looking up.

**VICKY BROWN** is a senior in the Creative Writing Department at the South Carolina Governor's School for the Arts and Humanities. Half Costa Rican and born in the sandhills of South Carolina, she splits her time between the U.S. and Costa Rica. Her writing has been published in *The Interlochen Review* and recognized nationally in the Scholastic Art & Writing Awards, where she has received a National Gold Medal for her Writing Portfolio. She intends to major in international relations with a concentration in Latin America and the Middle East.

**ALEXANDRA BYRNE** spent her childhood in Maplewood, New Jersey, making stories. Since then, nothing has really changed. She hopes to inspire others with her words and thoughts someday, but ultimately owes all she knows to the beautiful humans she is able to interact with each day.

**DANIELA CEJA** received two Gold Keys and a Silver Medal from the 2018 Scholastic Art & Writing Awards. She will be attending DePaul University in the fall to pursue a career in journalism and social activism.

**CRYSTAL CENTENO-PADILLA** is a Latina and a product of immigrants. She experiments with all sorts of art forms, including writing, to showcase what it is like being a first-generation Mexican-American: the beauty and the struggle.

**MICHAEL CHENG** is a high school senior from Wynnewood, Pennsylvania. He writes both poetry and prose for fun, and has been published in several literary magazines, such as *Blue Marble Review*. He won the Ralph Waldo Emerson Prize from *The Concord Review*, was a Science Olympiad National Gold

Medalist in Experimental Design, and also enjoys folding origami dragons.

**CATARINA CHUNG**, otherwise known as Cat, may be a medical student in Bergen County Academies, but she loves to write whenever she has the time. She is mainly interested in writing speculative pieces that make people think about what they may not normally consider. She has been published and has received multiple Scholastic Awards over the years.

. . . and then God laughed and sent **ANNIKA CLARK** into the world, kicking and screaming, just down the street from the federal penitentiary in Leavenworth, Kansas. She started running at eight months old and has been on the run ever since, living in eight different states over the course of her seventeen years. When she grows up, she wants to be a little kid, or at least write with the honesty of one.

**ELISEO CORONA** is a Latino writer from Elgin, Illinois. Identifying as a Catholic gay male, he advocates for the LGBT community and challenges traditional thinking with his modern prose and liberally expressed ideals.

**SHAUN-MARLEY DUNCAN** is constantly inspired by the diversity of culture, thought, and ideas that New York City and its people facilitate. Passionate discourse on social justice led by youth and minority groups is something that is finally being brought to center stage, and her writing is part of that effort. She believes that conversation is integral to change and hopes that her writing, while often humorous and satirical, generates serious and meaningful conversation.

**JACKSON EHRENWORTH** lives in New York City, though he spends much of his time outside of school mountaineering. A graduate of Avenues: The World School, Jackson is spending a gap year climbing four of the seven summits and studying wilderness emergency medicine.

**ISABELLA ERAULA** is a writer from Goose Creek, South Carolina. She writes about a variety of things, including her own experiences, serious topics, and historical events. A lot of her pieces can be experimental or a dedication to someone/something, and some have been published in writing anthologies like *The Battering Ram* and *The Good Juju Review*.

**ANI FREEDMAN** uses writing as a way to release all of the thoughts that swim back and forth in her brain, leaving her mind in a constant state of unrest. In "A Satire on Suburbia," she wanted to highlight the dry humor prevalent in her daily life, and to use a satirical approach to convey a reality she has experienced for the past 18 years. Ultimately, Ani wants her writing to make people think and open their eyes a little more, and "A Satire on Suburbia" was just a different way of doing so.

**ANANYA GANESH** hails from Atlanta, Georgia. She believes that her hyphenated heritage inspires her writing, which focuses on the unique perspectives of immigrant families, and hopes that her work will encourage young girls to proudly embrace their roots. Additionally, she runs a nonprofit organization focused on encouraging girls to become innovators and entrepreneurs.

**VICTORIA GONG**, a rising senior from Mississippi, is a STEM-oriented, piano-playing, noodle-loving writer with a habit of constructing run-on sentences and an ongoing dream of publishing a novel, which may or may not be realized. She will keep writing either way.

**GEORGIA GREENBLUM** is an avid journalist for *Grant Magazine* and her neighborhood magazines, carrying the titles of story editor and managing editor. Alongside writing, she won first in the nation in the "We the People" competition in 2018. Georgia loves to volunteer, keep active, and make music, and she looks forward to a career in medicine.

**SIMONE GULLIVER** is a rising senior from Montclair, New Jersey. She writes only to keep track of the 20,000 alternate reality possibilities running through her head at any given moment. If she's not reading or sleeping, you can probably find her petting dogs at the local park.

**CHARLIE HASTINGS** writes not to address politics, the world, or the environment. Charlie writes to address absurdity everywhere, in all forms. In Charlie's opinion, absurdity is what creates humor, imagination, and most of all, a good piece of writing.

**LUKE HERZOG**, a senior at Pacific Grove High School in California, wrote and published two full-length fantasy novels by the age of 13. In addition to receiving a Scholastic Art & Writing Awards Gold Medal in 2018, Luke was honored with an NCTE Achievement Award in Writing and was named a national finalist by the National YoungArts Foundation. Luke lives with his family and his dog, Pippin, named after J.R.R. Tolkien's mischievous hobbit.

Besides writing, **EILEEN HUANG** loves films, '80s music, and petting dogs—even though she's allergic to them. She views poetry as a voice for the voiceless and will continue to pursue her passion for writing at Yale University this fall.

**KALLEY HUANG** is a writer-in-progress who finds extreme delight in the Constitution and coffee. She was born and raised in New York City and cares deeply about racial equality, immigration reform, and criminal legal justice. In the fall, she will attend the University of North Carolina at Chapel Hill as a Robertson Scholar.

**NAHISHA JACKSON** is a 17-year-old radical queer black womanist. She enjoys making provocative and meaningful art (the more it makes people uncomfortable, the better!).

**SHEHARBANO JAFRY** developed a passion for writing when she started creating short stories at a young age. Now, as a rising senior, she continues to pursue this subject because she believes that words are the medium through which change can be fostered. Using her love for writing, Sheharbano has worked with nonprofit organizations to bring about that change.

**EMILY JIANG** attends a vocational high school in suburban New Jersey. She is an ailurophile, an amateur artist, and an avid writer of satire; her essays have appeared in the *Asbury Park Press*. With her limited leisure time, Emily dabbles in doodling as well as playing discordant piano pieces.

**NICK JOHNSON** is a writer, artist, and music lover. His physical disability and owning it as a part of his life have given him a unique outlook on life.

**MALACHI JONES** has been writing since elementary school. His work has been honored with several Scholastic Awards, culminating in 2018 with a prestigious Gold Medal Writing Portfolio. In 2016, he was a finalist for the National Student Poets Program, and in 2017 his work was published in *Rattle Young Poets Anthology* and in USC's Student Anthology, Writing South Carolina. This fall, he will be attending Columbia University on a full QuestBridge scholarship.

**RUKMINI KALAMANGALAM** is a graduate of Carnegie Vanguard High School and a current freshman at Emory University. Prior to her induction as Houston's Youth Poet Laureate (2017–18), she was on Houston's youth slam poetry team, Meta-Four Houston (2015–16). In 2018, she was named Youth Poet Laureate of the Southwest and a National Youth Poet Laureate Ambassador. She has been published by *The Houston Chronicle*, *ABC 13 Visions*, Mutabilis Press, *Houston Public Media*, and *The Apprentice Writer*.

Through her writing, **SARENA KUHN** is able to incorporate humor and adventure into her daily life. She hopes her work will encourage others to let their imaginations run wild and to explore the topics of identity, growth, and acceptance. Born and raised in Los Alamitos, California, she plans to continue her writing while studying at UC Berkeley this fall.

**JESSICA LIU** is a recipient of a Silver Medal in the Scholastic Art & Writing Awards from Madison, Wisconsin. A passionate advocate for what she believes in, she hopes that her writing will help amplify the voices of those who have been marginalized by society, such as the LGBTQ+ community and people of color, by exposing the discrimination they are subject to. She is also a dreamer, a connoisseur of notebooks, and a music addict.

**MEGAN LUNNY** writes for *The Courier-Times Intelligencer* and was the Bucks County High School Poet of 2017. Megan received a National Gold Medal in flash fiction from the Scholastic Art & Writing Awards in 2018. Her poetry has appeared in *Acumen: Young Poets.*

**ZAIN-MINKAH MURDOCK** strongly believes in James Baldwin, New York pizza, em-dashes, BTS, her succulent Alex, and—most important—love. She strongly believes that literature acts as both a mirror and a window into the human condition. The 18-year-old Jamaican-American poet plans to major in creative writing at Columbia University this fall.

Writing has become an outlet that **OSARUGUE OTEBELE** honestly cannot imagine life without. Whether it receives recognition or not, Osarugue's writing is her only way to express her truth. As a writer, she aims to make people aware of issues all over the world that carry even the smallest effects. If Osarugue cannot educate, explain, or make connections, then why should she write?

**MEGHNA PAMULA** is a high schooler from California. She enjoys art, reading, and writing. She has received a Gold Medal for her critical essay "The Permanence of Plastic."

**SOPHIE PAQUETTE** is from Bloomington, Indiana, and attends Interlochen Arts Academy, where she serves as an editor for *The Interlochen Review*. Her writing has appeared in or is forthcoming in *The Offing*, *Midwestern Gothic*, *Cosmonauts Avenue*, and others.

**LAILA SHADID** is Lebanese-American and lives in Cambridge, Massachusetts. She recently attended the New England Young Writers' Conference at the Bread Loaf Campus and writes often for her school newspaper as the projects editor. She is passionate about writing and hopes to further strengthen her skills in college.

**JULIA SPANDE** is a proud writer, activist, dancer, and New Yorker, in that order. She plans to combine her passion for equality and environmental advocacy with her love of writing at the University of Chicago this fall.

**MAXWELL SURPRENANT** is a rising ninth-grader at St. Sebastian's School in Needham, Massachusetts. Maxwell worked for three years as a kid reporter for Scholastic News Kids Press Corps and one year for *Sports Illustrated Kids*. His short film won Honorable Mention at the White House Student Film Festival, and he was honored to meet former President Barack Obama. Maxwell serves as the co-founder and executive of his own nonprofit, Catching Joy, Inc., which promotes volunteerism beginning with youth, teens, and families.

**ALEXANDRA SWERDLOFF** recently graduated from Boise High School in Boise, Idaho, and will attend Wellesley College in the fall of 2018. Her work, which includes personal essays, poetry, prose, and explores topics ranging from Jewish prayers to the AIDS crisis to the plight of teenage werewolves, received the Gold Medal Portfolio Award in the 2018 Scholastic Art & Writing Awards.

**AMRITA VETTICADEN** is a 16-year-old author from Phoenix, Arizona. She has three siblings and, unfortunately, no pets. In her free time, she enjoys reading fantasy novels (and writing her own), tasting new foods, and petting dogs.

**SAM WACHMAN**'s writing is largely about queer coming of age. It portrays queer teenage boys discovering their identities, grappling with their definitions of masculinity, and finding their places in life. Sam hopes that readers come away from his writing with a better idea of what it means to live in the liminal space between boyhood and manhood as a queer young person.

**TRINITI WADE** is an 18-year-old writer from Miami, Florida, whose work primarily explores various aspects of black girlhood, including sexuality, class, and femininity. Additionally, she highlights her own coming-of-age experiences in an often overlooked environment.

**TREVOR ZAVAC** is a spunky individual who considers himself a connoisseur of dry humor as well as an ardent patron for all things seriously silly. He prides himself on his quick wit and literal sense of humor, which he uses to write about his parallel universe in which all things appear to be the same with exception to their various hidden anachronisms.

**NATHAN ZHAO** is a rising senior at Wayland High School in Wayland, Massachusetts. An avid journalist, he enjoys reading and writing about the news, as well as debating and camping. His piece "Defrauding or Discriminating" delineates his argument as to why the 2016 election shifted in favor of Trump and explores the racial undertones of modern-day voter identification laws.

## EDUCATORS LIST

Leslie Arbetman
Auburn High School
Rockford, IL

Sandra Ascari
High Technology High School
Lincroft, NJ

Tara Bandman
Ardsley High School
Ardsley, NY

Latifa Barnett
Home School
Silver Spring, MD

TJ Beitelman
Alabama School of Fine Arts
Birmingham, AL

Chandra Boddie
Hollis F. Price Middle College
High School
Memphis, TN

Alyssa Boehringer
McKinney High School
McKinney, TX

Rachel Bohenick
Carnegie Vanguard High School
Houston, TX

Alan Brown
High Technology High School
Lincroft, NJ

Lisa Cicoria
Kearsarge Regional High School
North Sutton, NH

Marigrace Cirringone
Roslyn High School
Roslyn Heights, NY

Andrea Clark
Home School
Andover, KS

Murray Clark
Home School
Andover, KS

Rick Clark
East Lyme High School
East Lyme, CT

David Cornish
St. Sebastian's School
Needham, MA

Casey Curry
Howard W. Blake High School
Tampa, FL

Lori Danker
Prairie High School
Cedar Rapids, IA

Danielle DeTiberus
Charleston County School
of the Arts
North Charleston, SC

Angela Dixcy
Edgemont Jr. Senior High School
Scarsdale, NY

Caitlin Donovan
Hunter College High School
New York, NY

Jennifer Dracos-Tice
Westminster School
Atlanta, GA

Maura Dwyer
Stuyvesant High School
New York, NY

Michelle Dyer
BASIS School-Ahwatukee
Phoenix, AZ

Peter Elliott
John Cooper School
The Woodlands, TX

Travis Feldman
Choate-Rosemary Hall School
Wallingford, CT

Marcy Gamzon
School of the Arts
Rochester, NY

Nicholas Geary
Goose Creek High School
Goose Creek, SC

Diana Gentry
Hollis F. Price Middle College
High School
Memphis, TN

Sarah Getchell
Buckingham Browne & Nichols
High School
Cambridge, MA

Rocio Gonzalez
Bellevue High School
Bellevue, WA

Scott Gould
South Carolina Governor's School
for the Arts & Humanities
Greenville, SC

Tasha Graff
South Portland High School
South Portland, ME

Frederick Green
School for Advanced Studies-
North
Miami, FL

Sarah Gross
High Technology High School
Lincroft, NJ

Clay Guinn
St. John's School
Houston, TX

Brian Gutherman
Ardsley High School
Ardsley, NY

Patricia Halpin
Wayland High School
Wayland, MA

Francis Hammes
Charleston County School
of the Arts
North Charleston, SC

Elizabeth Hart
Charleston County School
of the Arts
North Charleston, SC

Shira Harwood
Manhasset Senior High School
Manhasset, NY

Chris Hawking
Grant High School
Portland, OR

Brittany Hennessey
South Elgin High School
South Elgin, IL

Erin Holtz
Oswego High School
Oswego, IL

John Howe
Madison West High School
Madison, WI

Jim Incorvaia
Harborfields High School
Greenlawn, NY

Ashley Jones
Alabama School of Fine Arts
Birmingham, AL

Jen Karetnick
Miami Arts Charter School
Miami, FL

Beth Larson
Menomonee Falls High School
Menomonee Falls, WI

Ariel Lewis
Miami Arts Charter School
Miami, FL

Caroline Lloyd
Dougherty Valley High School
San Ramon, CA

Ariel Maloney
Cambridge Rindge & Latin
High School
Cambridge, MA

Kwoya Maples
Alabama School of Fine Arts
Birmingham, AL

Jennifer McClain
Boise High School
Boise, ID

Christina Minecci
Lower Merion High School
Ardmore, PA

Mamie Morgan
South Carolina Governor's School
for the Arts & Humanities
Greenville, SC

Lara Naughton
New Orleans Center for
Creative Arts
New Orleans, LA

Mika Perrine
Interlochen Arts Academy
Interlochen, MI

Tracy Peterson
Flint Hill School
Oakton, VA

Emma Richardson
Mississippi School of Math &
Science
Columbus, MS

Colleen Rosini
Central Bucks High School East
Doylestown, PA

Susan Rothbard
Livingston High School
Livingston, NJ

Joe Sacksteder
Interlochen Arts Academy
Interlochen, MI

Eric Salehi
Montclair Kimberley Academy
Montclair, NJ

Rafael Sanchez
Berkeley Carroll School
Brooklyn, NY

Rodney Satterthwaite
Palo Alto High School
Palo Alto, CA

Ellon Sears
Rancho Solano Preparatory
School
Scottsdale, AZ

Katie Selfridge
Pacific Grove High School
Pacific Grove, CA

Nicholas Shelke
South High School
Denver, CO

Amanda Soesbee
North Mecklenburg High School
Huntersville, NC

Eileen Turo
Bethlehem Central High School
Delmar, NY

Richard Weems
Bergen County Academies
Hackensack, NJ

Rachel Weissenstein
St. John's School
Houston, TX

Kate Wernersbach
Apex Friendship High School
Apex, NC

Ron Widelac
Avenues: The World School
New York, NY

Karen Yoshihara-Ha
Los Alamitos High School
Los Alamitos, CA

Bethany Zilligen
Noblesville High School
Noblesville, IN

**MAGGIE TYNDALL**, *Maggie*, Drawing & Illustration. Grade 12, Age 17, Arendell Parrott Academy, Kinston, NC. Jana Miller, *Educator*

## AN EDUCATOR'S GUIDE TO *THE BEST TEEN WRITING OF 2018*

Use the works of these National Medalist teen writers to inspire discussion and guide writing exercises with students.

### 1. Short Story: Discussion on characterization and voice—35 minutes

**Goal**: Students explain how authors establish the voice of a narrator to create distinct characters who inform a reader of time, place, and mood.

**Activity**: Introduce the concept of a story's "voice" by having students discuss popular first-person narratives as well as close third-person narratives that are particularly different and compelling.

Next, choose a piece with a highly engaging character voice(s). As you're reading out loud, have students mark any points in the text where they notice specific character establishment through the tone of the prose, dialects, slang, humor, or other details. After you're finished, have students discuss the following:

• What does the author want us to know or understand about the narrator of this story?
• How does the separation of character voices establish a reliable—or unreliable—narrator?

In partners or groups, have students select a narrator and describe his or her personality. Then have them return to the text and find specific details (speech, thought, and interaction with others) to illustrate the narrator's personality and how it informs and shapes the narrative. Share student responses.

## 2. Short Story: Writing with focus on characterizing the narrative—35 minutes

**Goal**: Students restructure a narrative with another narrator, creating the same story with a different perspective.

**Activity**: Ask students to take on the voice of one of the other characters and tell the story from that point of view, filling in blanks that the original narrator left. Challenge students to use important characterizing details in the reading to give color to their entries.

## 3. Poetry: Writing with focus on form—30 minutes

**Goal**: Students write using different structural techniques.

**Activity**: Have students write two poems on one topic of their choosing. Begin with a prose poem, in which they write freely on that topic; then have them write another poem on the same topic with a focus on line breaks to emphasize changes in rhythm or highlight specific phrases. Discuss the differences after sharing the results.

## 4. Personal Essay/Memoir: Writing with a focus on structure and pacing—45 minutes

**Goal**: Students will write an organized and coherent memoir imitating the format of a *Best Teen Writing* piece.

**Activity**: Select a personal essay/memoir from the anthology to read out loud with your students. Talk about the format in which the memoir is written. Discuss the choices made and how those choices are inherently personal, therefore inherently suited to convey a personal essay.

Ask your students to write their own memoirs modeled after the memoir you have selected. Have the students share their work and discuss choices that each student makes, including how those choices convey something personal to the reader.

## 5. Genre-Shifting Exercise—40 minutes

**Goal**: Students will explore form's relationship to function by converting a piece in the anthology to another genre. For example, reimagine a play as a poem or a personal essay & memoir as a science fiction & fantasy piece.

**Activity**: Have the students choose a favorite piece in *The Best Teen Writing*, then have them reinterpret that work in another genre. Afterward, have the students compare the original to the genre-shifted piece and discuss how the same information is relayed through contrasting forms.

## 6. Blog Exercise—40 minutes and homework time

**Goal**: Students will use critical-thinking skills to offer critiques and analysis of specific works or the anthology as a whole.

**Activity**: Ask students to write a blog post expressing thoughts about a specific piece of their choosing. Posts will be sent to the Alliance for consideration to be included on the Alliance blog.
• Students should express their opinions, offering positive feedback or constructive criticism, on a specific work in *The Best Teen Writing*. Alternatively, they may discuss the anthology as a whole.

- Posts may be emailed to **info@artandwriting.org**, with the subject line "The Best Teen Writing of 2018 Student Blog Post."

**Educators**: Continue the discussion! Explore with your peers even more ways in which *The Best Teen Writing of 2018* can inspire students in your classroom! Visit the Vision and Voice website, presented by the National Writing Project, at **visionandvoice.nwp.org** to learn more.

## REGIONAL AFFILIATE ORGANIZATIONS

Recognizing young artists and writers begins with the Alliance's Affiliate Partners, which administer hundreds of art and writing regions across the country. They are responsible for bringing the Awards to local communities, educators, and students. Affiliates also work closely with local funders and universities* to provide scholarship opportunities for top recipients. With our Affiliates, we awarded nearly 90,000 works this year with regional Gold Keys, Silver Keys, and Honorable Mention awards. It is because of our Affiliate Partners' extraordinary dedication that the Scholastic Awards have been able to reach more participants and provide additional opportunities for creative teenagers across the country.

**Alaska**
Young Emerging Artists, Inc.

**Arizona**
Young Authors of Arizona

**California**
Community Memorial Museum of Sutter County
Pacific Grove Art Center
Yuba Sutter Arts

**Colorado**
Colorado Art Education Association

**Connecticut**
Connecticut Art Education Association
*University of Hartford's Hartford Art School*

* Local funders and universities are denoted in italics.

**Delaware**
Arts Center / Gallery at Delaware State University
Diamond State Branch, National League of American Pen
Women, Inc.
*Delaware State University; Delaware Division of the Arts;*
*National Endowment for the Arts*

**District of Columbia**
Writopia Lab

**Florida**
Educational Gallery Group (Eg2)
*Mary D. Fisher; The Armory Art Center; Marjorie Fisher*
Hillsborough County Public Schools
*Suncoast Credit Union Foundation; University of Tampa;*
*Hillsborough Education Foundation*
Miami-Dade County Public Schools
*Rubell Family Collection; Dade Art Educators Association*
Miami Writes
*The Miami-Dade County Fair & Exposition*
Northeast Florida Art Education Association
Pinellas County Schools
*Raymond James; Suncoasters of St. Petersburg*
Sarasota County Schools
*Sarasota County Board of Education; Ringling College of Art*
*& Design*
Young at Art Museum
*Joe DiMaggio Children's Hospital*

**Georgia**
Savannah College of Art and Design

## Hawai'i

Hawai'i State Department of Education
*Hawai'i State Foundation on Culture and the Arts*

## Idaho

Boise State Writing Project

## Illinois

Chicago Area Writing Project
Downers Grove North and South High Schools
*Community High School District 99*
John R. and Eleanor R. Mitchell Foundation / Cedarhurst
Center for the Arts
Mid-Central Illinois Art Region
*Springfield District 186; Springfield Art Association*

## Indiana

Clowes Memorial Hall, Butler Arts Center, and Hoosier
Writing Project at IUPUI
Fort Wayne Museum of Art
*PNC Bank*
South Bend Museum of Art
*The Stanley A. and Flora P. Clark Memorial Community Trust
Foundation; Jack and Yumiko Champaigne; Macy's; South
Bend Art Center Foundation; Walmart–Goshen IN; Zilky
Charitable Trust*

## Iowa

The Connie Belin & Jacqueline N. Blank International
Center for Gifted Education and Talent Development,
University of Iowa

*University of Iowa School of Art and Art History; The Grant Wood Art Colony; Iowa City UNESCO City of Literature*

## Kansas
Mark Arts
*Elizabeth B. Koch; K.T. Wiedemann Foundation, Inc.*
The Western Kansas Scholastic Art Awards
*Western Kansas Scholastic Art Association*

## Kentucky
Jefferson County Public Schools
*Fund for the Arts; KMAC Museum; Louisville Area Fiber and Textile Artists; Louisville Visual Art; University of Louisville Hite Art Institute*
Northern Kentucky Writing Region
Southern Kentucky Performing Arts Center (SKyPAC)
*Anonymous Donor*

## Louisiana
Greater New Orleans Writing Project
*The Clayton-Royer Family Fund*
Northwestern State University Writing Project

## Maine
Maine College of Art
The Southern Maine Writing Project at the University of Southern Maine
*The Betterment Fund*

## Massachusetts
School of the Museum of Fine Arts at Tufts University
*The Boston Globe Foundation*

## Michigan
College for Creative Studies
*Macomb Community College*
Kendall College of Art and Design of Ferris State University
*Howard Miller*

## Minnesota
Art Educators of Minnesota
*Regis Center for Art; Weisman Art Museum of the University of Minnesota*
Minnesota Writing Project
*University of Minnesota*

## Mississippi
Eudora Welty Foundation
*C Spire Foundation; Mississippi Department of Archives and History*
Mississippi Museum of Art
*Atoms Energy*

## Missouri
Greater Kansas City Writing Project
*Missouri Writing Projects Network; The University of Central Missouri*
Kansas City Art Institute

## Nebraska
Omaha Public Schools Art Department

## Nevada
The Nevada Museum of Art
Springs Preserve

**New Hampshire**
The National Writing Project in New Hampshire
The Scholastic Art Awards of New Hampshire
*The New Hampshire Institute of Art; The New Hampshire*
*Charitable Foundation Grant from The Putnam Fund*

**New Jersey**
Montclair Art Museum
Newark Public Library

**New Mexico**
New Mexico Art Education Association

**New York**
Arnot Art Museum
*Community Foundation of Elmira-Corning and the Finger*
*Lakes; Chemung Canal Trust Company; New York State*
*Council on the Arts; Chemung County; Town of Horseheads;*
*Anderson Foundation; ARTS Council of the Southern Finger*
*Lakes; Tripp-Rose Endowment Fund*
CNY Art Council
*M&T Charitable Foundation*
Hudson Valley Art Awards
*Sullivan, Dutchess, Orange, Ulster County BOCES;*
*Enlarged City School District of Middletown; Orange*
*County Arts Council*
NYC Scholastic Awards
*Parsons at Open Campus; Eugene Lang College of Liberal Arts*
Writopia Lab

## North Carolina
Asheville Art Museum
*Asheville Area Section of the American Institute of Architects*
Barton College
Charlotte-Mecklenburg Schools
*Mint Museum of Art; University of North Carolina at Charlotte*

## North Dakota
Plains Art Museum and the Red River Valley Writing Project at NDSU
*Wells Fargo; Fredrikson & Byron, P.A.*

## Ohio
Art Academy of Cincinnati
*Elsa Heisel Sule Foundation; The School for Creative and Performing Arts at The Erich Kunzel Center for Arts and Education; Summerfair Cincinnati; Jos. Berning Printing Co.*
The Cleveland Institute of Art
*Cuyahoga Arts and Culture*
Columbus College of Art & Design
K12 Gallery & TEJAS
Kent State University at Stark
Lorain County Regional Scholastic Arts Committee
*Nordson Corporation Foundation; Lorain County Community College Foundation; The Stocker Center Foundation*
Youngstown State University
*Youngstown State University Department of Art; Akron Children's Hospital Mahoning Valley; Community Foundation of the Mahoning Valley; Boardman Rotary; BOC Water Hydraulics Inc.; Trumbull County Educational Service Center*

**Oklahoma**
Tulsa Community College School of Visual and
Performing Arts
*Tulsa Community College Foundation*

**Oregon**
Oregon Art Education Association
*Pacific Northwest College of Art; Portland Art Museum;*
*Oregon State University; Central Oregon Community College;*
*Little Bird Arts*

**Pennsylvania**
California University of Pennsylvania
Commonwealth Charter Academy
East Central PA Scholastic Art Awards
Lancaster Museum of Art
Philadelphia Arts in Education Partnership
Philadelphia Writing Project
*Western PA Writing Project & The University of Pittsburgh*
*School of Education*

**Rhode Island**
Rhode Island Art Education Association

**South Dakota**
The University of South Dakota

**Tennessee**
Cheekwood Botanical Garden and Museum of Art
*The Tennessee Credit Union*
Memphis Brooks Museum of Art
*The Brooks Museum League*

Spring Hill Arts Center
*City of Spring Hill; Rippavilla Inc.*

## Texas
Harris County Department of Education
*Texas Art Supply; Midtown Arts & Theater Center Houston: MATCH*
SAY Sí (San Antonio Youth Yes)
St. Stephen's Episcopal School
Wayland Baptist University and the Abraham Family Art Gallery
*Plainview Cultural Arts Council, Inc.*

## Vermont
Brattleboro Museum & Art Center

## Virginia
Arlington County Public Schools
Fairfax County Public Schools
The Fine Arts Center for the New River Valley
*Town of Pulaski; Pulaski County; The Southwest Times; Shelor Motor Mile; Al's on First; Pulaski Yankees*
Visual Arts Center of Richmond

## Washington
Cornish College of the Arts
Schack Art Center
*BSNF Railway Foundation; Everett Cultural Arts Commission; The Boeing Company*

## Wisconsin

The Milwaukee Art Museum
*The Heller Foundation and Mary Ellen Heller in memory of Avis M. Heller; Peter and Debra Johnson; Vanguard Computers, Inc.; CompURent; an Anonymous Donor; James and Carol Wiensch*

Southeast Wisconsin Scholastic Writing Region
*Harborside Academy; Carthage College; University of Wisconsin—Parkside*

Still Waters Collective

## ACKNOWLEDGEMENTS

The Alliance for Young Artists & Writers gratefully acknowledges the thousands of educators who encourage students to submit their works to the Scholastic Art & Writing Awards each year and the remarkable students who have the courage to put their art and writing before panels of renowned jurors. We would like to especially recognize the National Writing Project for its far-reaching efforts in the writing community and its continued commitment to our program. In addition, our mission is greatly furthered through special partnerships with the National Writing Project, the National Art Education Association, the Association of Independent Colleges of Art and Design, and the NAACP's ACT-SO program.

## THANK YOU TO OUR SPONSORS

We express our sincere gratitude to Lindenmeyr Book Publishing Papers for donating the very paper these pages are printed on. Lindenmeyr also donated the paper for the *2018 Scholastic Art & Writing Awards National Catalog.*

Special thanks to: Scholastic Inc., The Maurice R. Robinson Fund, Command Web Offset Co., The New York Times, New York Life Foundation, The Herb Block Foundation, Blick Art Materials & Utrecht Art Supplies, Golden Artist Colors, Bloomberg Philanthropies, Entertainment Software Association Foundation, National Endowment for the Arts, Creative Circle, New York City Department of Cultural Affairs, Amazon Literary Partnership, and numerous other individual, foundation, and corporate funders. For the National Student Poets Program, special thanks to the Institute of Museum and Library Services and Poetry Foundation.

## SUPPORT THE SCHOLASTIC ART & WRITING AWARDS

Help support the Awards today! Your support will go a long way toward making the Scholastic Awards available for future generations of creative teens. Visit **artandwriting.org/donate** to make a tax-deductible contribution online, or send your gift to Alliance for Young Artists & Writers, 557 Broadway, New York, NY 10012. Thank you!